Color Vision and Colorimetry

THEORY AND APPLICATIONS

Color Vision and Colorimetry

THEORY AND APPLICATIONS

Daniel Malacara

SPIE PRESS

A Publication of SPIE—The International Society for Optical Engineering
Bellingham, Washington USA

Library of Congress Cataloging-in-Publication Data

Malacara, Daniel, 1937–
    Color vision and colorimetry : theory and applications / Daniel Malacara.
        p. cm.
    Includes bibliographical references and index.
    ISBN 0-8194-4228-3
    1. Color vision. 2. Colorimetry. I. Title.

QP483 .M353 2001
612.8'4—dc21   2001032290
                                                                                                          CIP

Published by

SPIE—The International Society for Optical Engineering
P.O. Box 10
Bellingham, Washington 98227-0010 USA
Phone: 360.676.3290
Fax: 360.647.1445
http//: www.spie.org

Table of Contents

Preface

This book is written for those who want to understand the basic principles of color vision and colorimetry but have no previous training in this field. The history of color, the main methods used to measure color, and their associated color systems are described. The human eye and its color detectors are also explained with some detail.

Chapter 1 introduces the reader to the main concepts, definitions, and the nature of color, including a definition of the main radiometric and photometric units related to color. Chapter 2 describes the key natural and artificial light sources used in colorimetry, and the standard illuminants used in colorimetry. In Chapter 3, the history and fundamentals of the trichromatic theory in the r, g, b system are described. In Chapter 4, the CIE color x, y, z specification system is introduced with all the basic mathematical tools for colorimetry. The mathematical procedure used to transform color from the r, g, b system to the CIE x, y, z system, which is not commonly available in most books, is described in some detail. This chapter contains many tables with colorimetric data and standards that can be of some use to those working in color measuring systems. Chapter 5 introduces the reader to the uniform color systems, describing their main differences and limitations. Special emphasis is placed on the CIE $L*U*V*$ and CIE $L*A*B*$ uniform color systems, which are now frequently used. In Chapter 6, the principles and mechanisms to produce and predict the color of colorant or pigment mixtures and their use is described. Chapter 7 covers some of the most common methods and instruments used for color measurements with their calibration procedures. Finally, in Chapter 8 the human eye is briefly described, with emphasis on the retinal detectors, but most importantly on the role of the cones in color vision.

At the end of each chapter, and at the end of the book, a good number of references are given for the benefit of those readers who wish to deepen their knowledge of this interesting field.

The author is grateful to Prof. Donald McCloud, Yobani Mejía and Didia P. Salas for their help and technical discussions.

Daniel Malacara
March 2002

Color Vision and Colorimetry

THEORY AND APPLICATIONS

Chapter 1
The Nature of Color

1.1 Introduction

Electromagnetic waves have many different wavelengths and frequencies that span a range known as the electromagnetic spectrum (Fig. 1.1). Light is a narrow range of electromagnetic waves that the eye can detect. Light of different wavelengths produces different perceptions of color. The longest wavelengths produce the perception of red, while the shortest ones produce the perception of violet. The visible, ultraviolet, and infrared spectral regions are classified in Table 1.1.

For many centuries, humans have been quite interested in color. However, the scientific study of color only goes back to Newton when he performed his classical experiment with a prism.

The sensation of color is produced by the physical stimulation of light detectors, called cones, in the human retina. The spectrum of colors produced by a prism is referred to as spectrally pure or monochromatic. They are related to the wavelength, as illustrated in Fig. 1.2. Different spectrally pure colors are said to have a different hue. A spectrally pure or monochromatic color can be produced by a single wavelength. For example, an orange color is associated with a wavelength of 600 nm. However, the same color can be produced with a combination of two light beams, one being red with a wavelength of 700 nm, and another being yellow with a wavelength of 580 nm, with no orange component. In this book, when we refer to a spectrally pure light beam it does not mean it is formed by a single wavelength beam, as in traditional physical or interferometry books. Instead, it means that it has the same color as the single wavelength light beam matching its color. Only with an instrument called a spectroscope can two or more components used to produce a color be identified by the eye. For this reason we say that the eye is a synthesizer device. In contrast, when the ear listens to an orchestra, the individual instruments producing the sound can be identified. Thus, we say that the ear is an analyzer.

Not all colors in nature are spectrally pure, since they can be mixed with white. In this manner, a mixture of red and white produces a pink color that goes from pure red (100% saturated) to white (0% saturated), depending on the relative amounts of red and white. All of these colors obtained by mixing a spectrally pure color with white are said to have the same *hue* but different *saturation*. The degree of saturation is called the *chroma*. Therefore, the relative amounts of a mixture of white and a spectrally pure color determine the color saturation, or chroma.

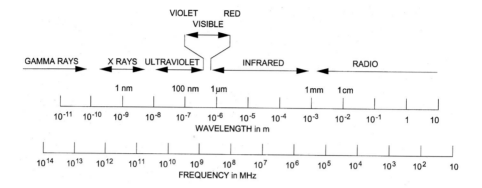

Figure 1.1 The electromagnetic spectrum.

Table 1.1 Ultraviolet, visible and infrared regions of the electromagnetic spectrum.

Spectral region	Range of wavelength in nm	Subregion
Ultraviolet	100-280	UV-C
	280-315	UV-B
	315-380	UV-A
Visible	380-430	Violet
	430-500	Blue
	500-520	Cyan
	520-565	Green
	465-580	Yellow
	580-625	Orange
	625-740	Red
Infrared	740-1400	Near IR
	1400-10000	Far IR

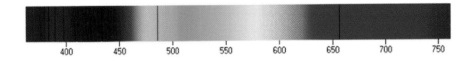

Figure 1.2 The visible spectrum with Hydrogen spectral lines as a reference.

Again, combinations of spectrally pure colors and white cannot produce all possible colors in nature. Let us consider two identical samples of a spectrally pure red color. If one of them is strongly illuminated and the other is almost in darkness, the two colors look quite different. In another example, if a pure red color is mixed with black, its appearance is different. In these two examples, the difference between the two red samples is its lightness or luminance.

In conclusion, any color has to be specified by three parameters, hue, saturation (or chroma) and luminance, or any other three equivalent parameters, as will be described in more detail later.

1.2 Newton's color experiment

The history of the first color theories and experiments is quite interesting, as described by MacAdam (1975) in his color review article. The first experiment in color, performed with a prism by Newton in 1671, demonstrated color dispersion. He used a triangular prism (Fig. 1.3) in a position so that a narrow beam of sunlight passed through the prism. When this beam was projected onto a screen, a band of light with different colors appeared, forming what he called a spectrum

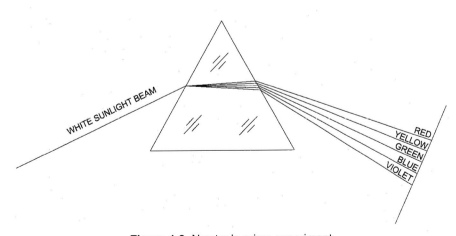

Figure 1.3 Newton's prism experiment.

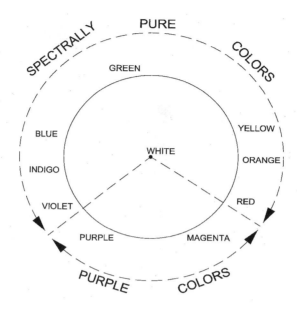

Figure 1.4 Newton's circle.

(ghost). Newton said that the spectrum was formed by seven colors: red, orange, yellow, green, blue, indigo, and violet, probably in close analogy with the seven musical notes. This experiment immediately suggested the idea that white light is formed by the superposition of all colors. To prove this idea, Newton used another prism to recombine all colors from the spectrum into a white beam of light. Newton was very careful to state that the spectrum colors are not the only ones in nature. For example, new colors can be obtained by diluting them with the addition of white. New colors can also be produced by increasing or reducing the intensity. In the case of paints, this is equivalent to mixing them with black paint, or to increasing the level of brightness.

Newton also tried to recombine only certain parts of the spectrum by blocking out some colors produced by the first prism, by means of diaphragms. When he recombined two different bands of color, a third color appeared, frequently, but not always, matching one between these two. By combining the two ends of the spectrum (red and violet) in different proportions, he was able to obtain a new gamut of purple colors ranging from red to violet.

The first color diagram was devised by Newton by drawing a circle with all pure spectral and purple colors around and the white at the center, as shown in Fig. 1.4. Colors formed by a mixture of the pure spectral colors and white are between the center and the circumference. Complementary colors are on opposite points with respect to the center. If this circle is made on a piece of cardboard and placed on the axis of a rotating top, all colors mix to produce the impression of a colorless gray.

1.3 Theories and experiments in color vision

After Newton's experiment, the next important contribution to the understanding of color came when Mariotte (1717) said that three colors are sufficient to produce any color when using the proper combination. This concept was introduced by Palmer (1777) in a manuscript that was discovered in 1956, adding to the concept of three different color receptors in the retina. In 1802, probably without being aware of the previous work by Palmer, Thomas Young refined the trichromatic theory of color, postulating that all colors in nature could be matched with three different colors that he called primary colors. He also postulated that the eye has three types of photoreceptors, one for each primary color. The problem with this theory is in determining which colors are primary.

The trichromatic theory of color was found satisfactory, but it did not explain many details. About fifty years later Hermann von Helmholtz (1852, 1866) revived and improved Young's ideas by adding more details based on experiments. For this reason, the trichromatic theory of light is now known as the Young-Helmholtz theory. At about this time, many other researchers were doing interesting optical color experiments (Peirce, 1877; Rayleigh, 1881).

Edwald Hering observed that there is no bluish yellow or yellowish blue and determined that yellow and blue are opposite colors. In the same manner, red and green are opposite colors. Hering proposed a theory to explain this with four colors—red, yellow, green, and blue—as primaries. (Later, we will see that although this theory is not correct in detail, it has some interesting concepts that deserve consideration.) He assumed that the brain has a detector for yellow and blue light, followed by a classifier to determine the relative luminance of the two colors. In the same manner, he assumed another brain detector for red and green light, followed by another classifier to determine the relative quantities of these two colors. Further, he assumed another classifier for white and black.

Almost simultaneously with the work of Helmholtz, in 1861, James Clerk Maxwell (1856, 1857, 1860, 1885) studied the perception of color and performed an experiment, as illustrated in Fig. 1.5, to produce a fully colored image, thus proving the Young-Helmholtz theory. He took three black and white photographs of the same scene, by placing three different colored filters in front of each of the three shots. Then, he projected the three pictures simultaneously with three projectors and each of the three colored filters in front of each projector. He assumed that the black and white photographic emulsion was equally sensitive to the three colors used. Unfortunately, this basic assumption was far from being correct, but it was compensated for in the final result. Evans (1961) describes why Maxwell obtained good results in spite of this. In 1890, Arthur Koening assumed from the previous hypothesis by his predecessors that there are three color

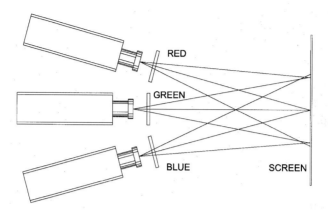

Figure 1.5 Maxwell's experiment.

detectors in the eye, one for red, one for green, and one for blue. In 1888, Frederick E. Ives repeated Maxwell's experiment using photographic emulsions that were sensitive over the entire luminous spectrum, and set up the main principles that led to modern color photography.

The "zone" color theories combine the opponent and trichromatic models. According to these theories the trichromatic signals produced by the cones in the retina are sent to the brain, where they are converted into three opponent signals, two of them chromatic and one achromatic. These theories have now been discarded.

A more recent model is the "retinex" theory developed by Edwin Land (1959, 1977) and described by Kaiser and Boynton (1966). Land made an impressive modification to the three projectors experiment by Maxwell. He was able to

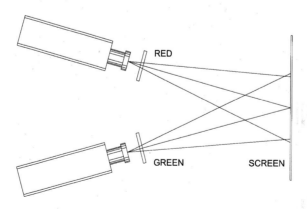

Figure 1.6 Edwin Land's experiment.

project a full-color scene with only two colors, like red and green or even red and white, as shown in Fig. 1.6. A detailed analysis of this experiment and the theory behind it is found in the articles by Land (1959) and by Judd (1960). Land's theory and experiment can explain our capacity to observe undistorted colors under a wide variety of illumination conditions. For example, a white piece of paper appears to be white under daylight illumination and under an incandescent tungsten lamp. This remarkable process is known as chromatic adaptation (Judd, 1951 and 1952).

To complicate the color vision models even more, it is easy to show that flickering white light, produced by the alternation of bright and dark fields, can produce color sensations that depend on the flickering frequency. If this frequency is sufficiently high, with more than about 60 Hz, fusion occurs and no flickering effects are observed. By means of flickering at frequencies smaller than 60 Hz the "subjective" or Fetchner colors can be produced. These can be produced with rotating disks with many different patterns. Probably the best known is the Benham (1894) disc, shown in Fig 1.7. Colored rings are observed when rotated with a speed of 5 to 10 revolutions per second. Since the pattern is not rotationally symmetrical, different colors are observed not only for different speeds, but also for different directions of rotation.

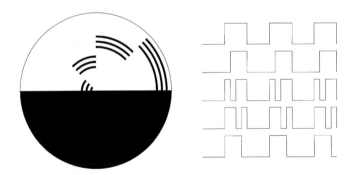

Figure 1.7 Benham's disc with the light intensity distribution as a function of time.

Figure 1.8 The McCollough effect. The first and second patterns are observed for about 5 to 10 minutes, with alternating fixations of 10 seconds. Then, the third pattern is observed. Pale green appears on the left half and pale red on the right half.

Another interesting effect related to flickering is the McCollough effect illustrated in Fig 1.8. The first two patterns with vertical and horizontal lines, respectively, should be observed for about ten minutes in an alternating manner, for about ten seconds each. Then, the third pattern is observed. Pale green will be seen where the vertical lines are and pale red where the horizontal lines are.

In conclusion, the perception of color is not a purely physical mechanism but is also physiological and psychological.

1.4 Some radiometric and photometric units

Many concepts in color theory cannot be fully understood without the clear definitions of some radiometric and photometric units. The notation of these quantities is extremely varied and frequently inconsistent and confusing, so some quantities may appear strange if compared with certain books.

In this section we will go to the tedious work of defining some of the most important quantities used in colorimetry studies, before going to more interesting matters. The most basic definition is that of *radiant flux* φ_R, which is the radiant energy per unit time (power) transported by a light beam, measured in watts. The *irradiance* $\overline{W}$ is the total integrated radiant flux for all wavelengths, in watts, per unit area falling on an illuminated body as defined by

$$\overline{W} = \frac{\text{radiant flux}}{\text{area}} = \frac{d\phi_R}{dA}. \tag{1.1}$$

The *spectral irradiance* $W(\lambda)$, defined as the irradiance per unit wavelength interval, is related to the irradiance $\overline{W}$ by the relation

$$\overline{W} = \int_{-\infty}^{+\infty} W(\lambda) \, d\lambda. \tag{1.2}$$

Similarly, the *radiance* $\overline{P}$ of a luminous surface is the total integrated radiant flux for all wavelengths, in watts, per steradian, per unit of perceived area of the luminous surface as follows:

$$\overline{P} = \frac{\text{radiant flux per steradian}}{\text{perceived area}} = \frac{1}{\cos\theta} \frac{d^2\phi_R}{dA \, d\Omega}, \tag{1.3}$$

where the perceived area is equal to the actual area A of the source, multiplied by the cosine of the angle θ between the line of sight and the normal to the source. The radiance is a function of the observing direction θ. The *spectral radiance* $P(\lambda)$, defined as the radiance per unit wavelength interval, is related to the radiance $\overline{P}$ by

$$\overline{P} = \int_{-\infty}^{+\infty} P(\lambda) \, d\lambda \; . \tag{1.4}$$

Thus, the radiance is a function of the observation direction as well as of the wavelength. When the light enters the eye, a luminous stimulus is produced. The *luminous flux* φ_L is the equivalent of the radiant flux, but evaluated according to the magnitude of the luminous stimulus it produces, measured in lumens.

The *luminance* $\overline{L}$ of a luminous surface is defined as the total integrated luminous flux for all wavelengths emitted per steradian in a given direction per unit of perceived area of the luminous surface, as follows:

$$\overline{L} = \frac{\text{luminous flux per steradian}}{\text{perceived area}} = \frac{1}{\cos\theta} \frac{d^2\phi_L}{dA \; d\Omega} \; . \tag{1.5}$$

As the radiance, the luminance is a function of the observation direction. The *spectral luminance* $L(\lambda)$, defined as the luminance per unit wavelength interval, is related to the luminance $\overline{L}$ by

$$\overline{L} = \int_{-\infty}^{+\infty} L(\lambda) \, d\lambda \tag{1.6}$$

Given a certain spectral distribution, the luminance is directly proportional to the radiance, with a linear relation between them. However, the response of the eye is not linear with these two quantities. Another quantity, frequently used, called the *lightness*, is not linear with the luminance or the radiance, but is more linear with the eye response, as will be described in Chapter 5.

The *brightness* is a more subjective term than the luminance or the lightness. The luminance is defined for an ideal average observer. On the other hand, the brightness is the actual perceived luminance for a given observer and a given observed object region. As an example, when observing a sharp frontier between an evenly illuminated surface and a dark field, some fringes called Mach bands are observed. Then, the luminance is constant over the whole surface, but the brightness is not.

The *luminous efficiency* $\overline{\sigma}(\lambda)$ is defined by the ratio of the luminance to the radiance as

$$\overline{\sigma} = \text{luminous efficiency} = \frac{L}{P} \; . \tag{1.7}$$

The *spectral luminous efficiency* $\sigma(\lambda)$ is defined by the ratio of the spectral luminance $L(\lambda)$ to the spectral radiance $P(\lambda)$ at the wavelength λ, and thus it is a function of the wavelength, as follows:

$$\sigma(\lambda) = \frac{L(\lambda)}{P(\lambda)} .\qquad (1.8)$$

The spectral luminous efficiency for the eye (Gibson and Tindall, 1923), also known as *luminous sensitivity*, is defined in an analogous manner. This function has a peak value located at a wavelength of 555 nm, as described in detail in Sec. 1.5. One watt of radiant energy at the wavelength of 555 nm is equivalent to 683 lumens. The *relative spectral luminous efficiency* $V(\lambda)$ is defined as the luminous efficiency divided by its peak value at a wavelength of 555 nm. Thus, the maximum value is equal to one. Using this definition, the *spectral luminous efficiency* $\sigma(\lambda)$ in watts per lumen of a light source at the wavelength λ is

$$\sigma(\lambda) = 683 \, V(\lambda),\qquad (1.9)$$

and the luminance of a polychromatic light source is

$$\overline{L} = \int_{-\infty}^{+\infty} \sigma(\lambda) \, P(\lambda) \, d\lambda = 683 \int_{-\infty}^{+\infty} V(\lambda) \, P(\lambda) \, d\lambda .\qquad (1.10)$$

Hence, the luminous efficiency of a polychromatic light source can be shown as:

$$\overline{\sigma} = \frac{\displaystyle\int_{0}^{\infty} \sigma(\lambda) \, P(\lambda) \, d\lambda}{\displaystyle\int_{0}^{\infty} P(\lambda) \, d\lambda} = 683 \frac{\displaystyle\int_{0}^{\infty} V(\lambda) \, P(\lambda) \, d\lambda}{\displaystyle\int_{0}^{\infty} P(\lambda) \, d\lambda} .\qquad (1.11)$$

At all wavelengths, the *reflectance* $\overline{\rho}$ of a diffuse object is the quotient of the total radiant flux, reflected from the object in all directions, divided by the total radiant flux incident on the object. Since the object is diffuse, the reflected light travels in all directions, even if the illuminating beam travels in a single direction. The *spectral reflectance* $\rho(\lambda)$ is the reflectance per unit wavelength interval and it is a function of the wavelength. Thus, they are related by

$$\overline{\rho} = \int_{-\infty}^{+\infty} \rho(\lambda) \, d\lambda .\qquad (1.12)$$

The *luminous reflectance* $\bar{R}$ is the quotient of the total polychromatic reflected luminous flux divided by the incident luminous flux, assuming a standard illuminant, for example, the CIE illuminant D_{65}, to be described in Chapter 2. This luminous reflectance has different values for different standard illuminants. The *spectral luminous reflectance* $R(\lambda)$ is defined as the luminous reflectance per unit wavelength interval, so that

$$\bar{R} = \int_{-\infty}^{+\infty} R(\lambda) \, d\lambda . \tag{1.13}$$

At all wavelengths, the *transmittance* $\bar{\tau}$ of a transparent object is the quotient of the total radiant flux transmitted by the object divided by the total radiant flux incident on the object. The spectral transmittance $\tau(\lambda)$ is the transmittance per unit wavelength interval and it is a function of the wavelength. They are related by

$$\bar{\tau} = \int_{-\infty}^{+\infty} \tau(\lambda) \, d\lambda . \tag{1.14}$$

The *luminous transmittance* T is the quotient of the total polychromatic transmitted luminous flux divided by the incident luminous flux, assuming a standard illuminant. This luminous transmittance has different values for different standard illuminants. The *spectral luminous transmittance* $T(\lambda)$ is defined as the luminous reflectance per unit wavelength interval, so that

$$\bar{T} = \int_{-\infty}^{+\infty} T(\lambda) \, d\lambda . \tag{1.15}$$

With these definitions we are ready to describe the color sensitivity of the eye.

1.5 Color sensitivity of the eye

When the light enters the eye and arrives at the retina, the energy is absorbed by the photopigments located at the tips of the rods and cones. These cones and rods are at the back of the retina near a black layer known as the choroids, which contains one hundred million rods and five million cones. The center of the retina called the fovea is devoid of rods, but here the density of cones is greater.

The luminous sensitivity, as discussed in Sec. 1.4, is defined as the ratio of the luminance to the radiance, and it is a function of the wavelength of light. This sensitivity is a constant for all luminance levels. To measure the spectral luminous efficiency of the eye, we must find a procedure to determine when two monochromatic fields with different colors have the same luminance. Then, using the proper procedure, a luminous match is made on a split field with two colors. If the radiance is measured in these two fields using color photometric methods (Abney and Festing, 1886), their *relative luminous efficiency*, or *luminous sensitivity*, is found. A direct brightness match yields unreliable results due to the difference in color and leads to serious additive failures (Uchikawa et al., 1984; Elzinga and de Weert, 1986) as described by Boynton (1996). A much better method is to alternate between the two fields with different colors with a frequency of about 10 to 15 Hz, and then change the brightness of one of them until the alternating flickering is minimized. Developed by Ives (1912), it is known as the flicker method and it is quite reliable. The flicker method is further described in Chapter 7.

When doing these measurements, it is found that there are two different luminous sensitivities for low and high illumination levels, as shown in Fig. 1.9. One corresponds to the sensitivity of the rods and the other to the sensitivity of the cones. One of these two eye sensitivities, or luminosity functions, is for day vision $V(\lambda)$, or photopic, and the other for night vision $V'(\lambda)$, or scotopic.

The *photopic curve* $V(\lambda)$ was measured by several authors, for example, with the flicker methods by Coblentz and Emerson (1918) and with the step-by-step methods of heterochromatic photometry by Hyde et al., (1918). It was shown by Ives (1912) that the two methods give similar results for a field of two degrees if the wavelength is not below 500 nm. The Commission Internationale de l'Éclairage (CIE) in 1924 (CIE, 1926) adopted a photopic curve $V(\lambda)$ based on the work by Gibson and Tyndall (1923) and previous workers. According to recent measurements, a photopic curve $V(\lambda)$ slightly different in the violet end of the spectrum is obtained. A corrected version was later proposed by Judd

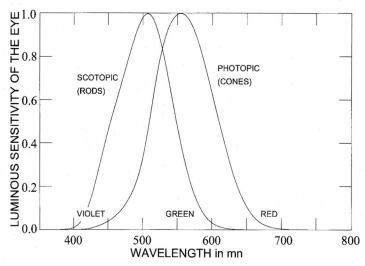

Figure 1.9 Luminous sensitivities of the photopic and scotopic eye.

(1951). However, the change has not been made because all present-day photometry has been based on this function for more than half a century.

The *scotopic curve* $V'(\lambda)$ was adopted by the CIE in 1951 (CIE, 1951). The measurements were taken with monochromatic stimuli by the method of visual comparison with low brightness in a field of 10 deg (Crawford, 1949), and on visual thresholds viewed eccentrically with more than 5 deg from the fovea (Wald, 1945) with complete dark adaptation. This function is quite sensitive to the age of the observer, who is assumed to be younger than 30 years old. The values for these functions are normalized to a maximum value of one, as shown in Table 1.2.

We can see that for daylight vision the maximum luminous efficiency is for a color corresponding to a wavelength of 555 nm (yellow), while for night vision this maximum efficiency shifts to the blue at about 505 nm.

1.6 How materials are colored or modify color

The color of the light emitted by a hot or warm body is defined by its emission spectrum. Every chemical element or compound has a characteristic element that spectroscopists use to identify it. A particular kind of luminous body is called the blackbody and will be studied with some detail in Chapter 2. The brightness and color of the blackbody depends on its temperature. The higher its temperature, the greater its brightness and the bluer the light it emits. At low temperatures, the brightness is low and its light is reddish or infrared. This body does not emit any light when it reaches the extremely low temperature of -273 centigrade (Celsius). This is why the scale of "absolute temperatures," or Kelvin, has been defined as the Celsius temperature plus 273.

Any luminous colored body has a color that can be considered as the superposition of a monochromatic spectrally pure color and white. The wavelength corresponding to the color of the spectrally pure component is said to be the "dominant wavelength." The temperature of the blackbody with the same dominant color is defined as the "color temperature" of the luminous body. These concepts will be studied with more detail in Chapter 2.

When the object is illuminated, the light is (a) transmitted, (b) reflected, (c) scattered, and (d) absorbed. These four processes can change the color of the light, since not all wavelengths are equally transmitted, reflected, scattered, or absorbed. If the atoms, molecules, or particles in a body have much smaller separations than the wavelength of light, the scattering process is not present. Then, we have a transparent body, where only the reflection, absorption, and transmission take place. The atoms and molecules forming the material being illuminated have certain resonance frequencies (wavelengths) where they absorb the light and heat the material, instead of reflecting or transmitting it. Single atoms have their resonances on the visible and ultraviolet. On the other hand, molecules have their resonances in the infrared.

In general, materials are formed by many different kinds of atoms and molecules. This gives them a characteristic spectral transmission or reflection. Thus, each opaque or transparent material has its own characteristic color when illuminated with white light.

1.7 Absorption and interference filters

When a beam of light passes through a transparent body some of the light is transmitted, some is reflected, and some is absorbed. These three processes are a function of the wavelength. A transparent plate made out of a material with absorption capability in the visible wavelengths is an absorption filter. They are usually made out of a colored glass or plastic, which in turn is made by adding a dye to them. The optical quality of plastic filters is lower than that of glass filters, but they are cheaper. The gelatin Wratten filters, manufactured by Kodak some years ago, were very popular and inexpensive. The most common colored glass filters now available are made out of colored Schott glass. These filters are more

Table 1.2 Relative spectral luminous efficiency functions of the eye.

Wave-length in nm.	$V(\lambda)$ Photopic	$V'(\lambda)$ Scotopic	Wave-length in nm.	$V(\lambda)$ Photopic	$V'(\lambda)$ Scotopic
380	0.0000	0.0006	450	0.0380	0.4550
385	0.0001	0.0011	455	0.0480	0.5130
390	0.0001	0.0022	460	0.0600	0.5670
395	0.0002	0.0045	465	0.0739	0.6200
400	0.0004	0.0093	470	0.9010	0.6960
405	0.0006	0.0185	475	0.1126	0.7340
410	0.0012	0.0348	480	0.1390	0.7930
415	0.0022	0.0904	485	0.1693	0.8510
420	0.0040	0.0966	490	0.2080	0.9040
425	0.0073	0.1436	495	0.2586	0.9490
430	0.0116	0.1998	500	0.3230	0.9820
435	0.0168	0.2625	505	0.4073	0.9980
440	0.0230	0.3281	510	0.5030	0.9970
445	0.0298	0.3931	515	0.6082	0.9750

Table 1.2 Continued.

Wave-length in nm.	V(λ) Photopic	V'(λ) Scotopic	Wave-length in nm.	V(λ) Photopic	V'(λ) Scotopic
520	0.7100	0.9350	650	0.1070	0.0007
525	0.7932	0.8800	655	0.0816	0.0004
530	0.8620	0.8110	660	0.0610	0.0003
535	0.9148	0.7330	665	0.0446	0.0002
540	0.9540	0.6500	670	0.0320	0.0001
545	0.9803	0.5640	675	0.0232	0.0001
550	0.9949	0.4810	680	0.0170	0.0001
555	1.0000	0.4020	685	0.0119	0.0000
560	0.9950	0.3288	695	0.0057	0.0000
565	0.9786	0.2639	700	0.0041	0.0000
570	0.9520	0.2076	705	0.0029	0.0000
575	0.9154	0.1602	710	0.0021	0.0000
580	0.8700	0.1212	715	0.0015	0.0000
585	0.8163	0.0899	720	0.0010	0.0000
590	0.7570	0.0655	725	0.0007	0.0000
595	0.6949	0.0469	730	0.0005	0.0000
600	0.6310	0.0331	735	0.0004	0.0000
605	0.5668	0.0231	740	0.0002	0.0000
610	0.5030	0.0159	745	0.0002	0.0000
615	0.4412	0.0109	750	0.0001	0.0000
620	0.3810	0.0074	755	0.0001	0.0000
625	0.3210	0.0050	760	0.0001	0.0000
630	0.2650	0.0033	765	0.0000	0.0000
635	0.2170	0.0022	770	0.0000	0.0000
640	0.1750	0.0015	775	0.0000	0.0000
645	0.1382	0.0010	780	0.0000	0.0000

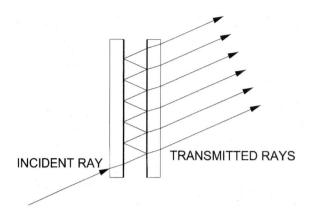

Figure 1.10 A Fabry-Perot interferometer.

costly but they have good quality and a large diversity of transmittance curves that can be classified as follows:

(a) Color temperature conversion filters that can lower (reddish filters) or elevate (bluish filters) the color temperature of light sources, for example, tungsten lamps.
(b) Heat absorbing filters, used in illumination systems to block out the heating infrared radiation without attenuating the visible light by any noticeable amount.
(c) Long- and short-wavelength pass filters. Their edge is not sharp as in the interference filters to be described later.
(d) Band-pass filters, with a wide wavelength transmission band.

An interference filter transmits part of the light and reflects the rest. The working principle is based on the Fabry-Perot interferometer, as illustrated in Fig. 1.10. The multiple light beam reflections between the two flat and partially reflecting surfaces produce many transmitted beams. These beams interfere, producing a very characteristic spectral distribution on the transmitted beam as well as on the reflected beams. Due to the energy conservation principle, at any wavelength the energy on the transmitted beam plus the energy on the reflected beam equals the energy on the incident beam. The spectral transmittance of these filters is as shown in Fig. 1.11.

We see that the spectral transmittance is formed by a series of spectral lines spaced with equal wavelength intervals. This separation $\Delta\lambda$ between the lines depends on the separation of d between the two partially reflecting mirrors, as given by

$$\Delta\lambda = \frac{\lambda^2}{2n\mathrm{d}} \quad , \tag{1.16}$$

where n is the refractive index for the medium between the two flat semireflecting mirrors. A typical spectral transmission for an interference filter is illustrated in Fig. 1.12. Absorption and interference filters can be combined to isolate a single spectral line.

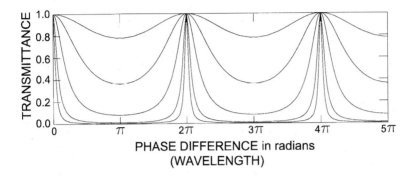

Figure 1.11 Spectral transmittance curves for a Fabry-Perot interferometer, with different values of the reflectivity of the partially reflecting mirrors. The optical path difference is that between two consecutively reflected beams, which is a function of the wavelength.

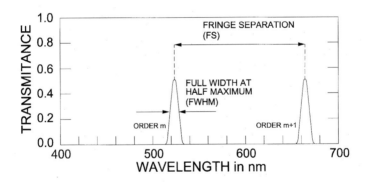

Figure 1.12 A typical spectral transmittance curves for an interference filter.

References

Abney W. D. W., and E. R. Festing, "Colour Photometry," *Philosophical Transactions of the Royal Society of London*, **177**, pp. 423–456 (1886).

Benham C. E., "Notes," *Nature (London)*, **51**, pp. 113–114 (1894).

CIE, Commission Internationale de l'Éclairage Proceedings, 1924, Cambridge, Cambridge University Press (1926).

Boynton R. M., "History and Current Status of a Physiologically Based System of Photometry and Colorimetry," *J. Opt. Soc. Am. A*, **13,** pp. 1609–1621 (1996).

CIE., *Bureau Central de la CIE*, Paris, **1**, Sec 4; Vol 3, pp. 37 (1951).

Coblentz W. W., "Relative Sensitivity of the Average Eye to Light of Different Colors," *Bull. Bur. Stand.*, **14**, pp. 167–236 (1918).

Crawford B. H., "The Scotopic Visibility Function," *Proc. Phys. Soc. of London*, **B62,** pp. 321–334, (1949).

Elzinga C. H. and C. M. M. de Weert, "Spectral Sensitivity Functions Derived from Color Matching: Implications of Intensity Invariance for Color Vision Models," *J. Opt. Soc. Am. A.*, **3,** pp. 1183–1191 (1986).

Evans R. M., "Maxwell's Color Photograph," *Scientific American*, Vol. 205, November, pp. 112–128 (1961).

Gibson K. S. and E. P. T. Tindall, "Visibility of Radiant Energy," *Sci. Pap. Bur. Stand.*, **19**, pp. 131–191 (1923).

Hyde E. P., W. E. Forsythe and F. E. Cady, "The Visibility of Radiation," *Astrophys. J.*, **48**, 65–88 (1918).

Ives F. E., "Studies in the Photometry of Lights of Different Colours. I. Spectral Luminosity Curves Obtained by the Equality of Brightness Photometer and Flicker Photometer Under Similar Conditions," *Phil. Mag. Ser. 6*, **24,** pp. 149–188 (1912).

Judd D. B., "Report of the U. S. Secretariat Committee on Colorimetry and Artificial Daylight," in *Proceedings of the 12th Session of the CIE, Stockholm*, Technical Committee No. 7, Bureau Central de la CIE, Paris, (1951).

Judd D. B., "Appraisal of Land's Work on Two Primary Color Projections," *J. Opt. Soc. Am.*, **50**, pp. 254–268 (1960). Reprinted in *Selected Papers in Colorimetry—Fundamentals*, D. L. MacAdam, Editor, SPIE Milestone Series, Volume MS77 (1993).

Judd D. B., "Object-Color Changes from Daylight to Incandescent Filament Illumination," *Illuminating Engineering*, **47**, pp. 221–233 (1952). Reprinted in *Selected Papers in Colorimetry—Fundamentals*, D. L. MacAdam, Editor, SPIE Milestone Series, Volume MS77, (1993).

Kaiser P. K. and R. M. Boynton, *Human Color Vision, Second Edition*. pp. 508, Optical Society of America, Washington DC (1996).

King-Smith P. E., and J. R. Webb, "The Use of Photopic Saturation in Determining the Fundamental Spectral Sensitivity Curves," *Vision Research*, **14**, pp. 421–429 (1974).

Land E. H., "Experiments in Color Vision," *Scientific American*, Vol. 200, May (1959).

Land E. H., "The Retinex Theory of Color Vision," *Scientific American*, Vol. 237, December, pp. 108–128 (1977).

MacAdam D. L., "Color Essays," *J. Opt. Soc. Am.*, 65, pp. 483–493 (1975).

Mariotte E., *Oeubres*, Van de Aa, Leyden, (1717).

Maxwell J. C., "Theory of the Perception of Colors," *Phil. Trans. Roy. Scottish Soc. of Arts*, **4**, pp. 394–400 (1856). Reprinted in *Selected Papers in Colorimetry —Fundamentals*, D. L. MacAdam, Editor, SPIE Milestone Series, Volume MS77 (1993).

Maxwell J. C., "The Diagram of Colors," *Phil. Trans. Roy. Soc. of Edinbugh*, **21**, pp. 275–298 (1857). Reprinted in *Selected Papers in Colorimetry— Fundamentals*, D. L. MacAdam, Editor, SPIE Milestone Series, Volume MS77 (1993).

Maxwell J. C., "On the Theory of Compound Colours and the Relations of the Colours of the Spectrum," *Philosophical Transactions of the Royal Society of London*, **150**, pp. 57–84 (1860).

Maxwell J. C., "Experiments on Colours, as Perceived by the Eye, with Remarks on Colour–Blindness," *Trans. Roy. Soc. of Edinburgh*, **21**, pp. 275–298 (1885).

Newton I., "New Theory About Light and Colors," *Phil. Trans. Roy. Soc. Of London*, **80**, pp. 3075–3087 (1671). Reprinted in D. L. MacAdam, Editor, *Selected Papers in Colorimetry—Fundamentals*, SPIE Milestone Series, Volume MS77 (1993).

Palmer G., "Theory of Colors and Vision," Leacroft, pp. 41–47, London, (1777). Reprinted in *Selected Papers in Colorimetry—Fundamentals*, D. L. MacAdam, Editor, SPIE Milestone Series, Volume MS77 (1993).

Peirce C. S., "Note on the Sensation of Color," *American J. of Science and Arts*, **13**, pp. 247–251 (1877).

Rayleigh L., "Experiments on Colour," *Nature*, **25**, pp. 64–66 (1881).

Uchikawa K., H. Uchikawa, and P. K. Kaiser, "Luminance and Saturation of Equally Bright Colors," *Color Res. Appl.*, **9**, pp. 5–14 (1984).

von Helmholtz H., "Physiological Optics," in *Handbuch der Physiologischen Optik*, 1866. Reprinted in *Selected Papers in Colorimetry—Fundamentals*, D. L. MacAdam, Editor, SPIE Milestone Series, Volume MS77 (1993).

von Helmholtz H., "On the Theory of Compound Colours," *Philosophical Magazine Series 4*, **4**, pp. 519–534 (1852).

Wald G. "The Spectral Sensitivity of the Human Eye: A Spectral Adaptometer,"*J. Opt. Soc. Am.*, **35**, pp. 187–196 (1945).

Westheimer G., "The Maxwellian View," *Vision Research*, **6**, pp. 669–682 (1966).

Young T., "On the Theory of Light and Colours," *Philosophical Transactions of the Royal Society of London*, **92**, pp. 20–21 (1802). Reprinted in *Selected Papers in Colorimetry—Fundamentals*, D. L. MacAdam, Editor, SPIE Milestone Series, Volume MS77 (1993).

Chapter 2
Light Sources and Illuminants

2.1 Introduction

The perceived color of an illuminated object depends not only on its intrinsic color or spectral reflectivity, but also on the power spectrum of the light source. In this chapter, we will study some of the most important light sources used in colorimetric studies. General descriptions of light sources can be found in many publications (Levin, 1979; Elenbaas, 1972; LaRocca, 1995; Malacara and Morales, 1988).

2.2 Blackbody radiation

Any nonmonochromatic light source can be characterized by its spectral power distribution—the total amount of power that it emits in a small unit interval of wavelength or frequency. Different curves are obtained in both cases, but the most frequently used is the power per unit of wavelength interval. A blackbody has no color—that is, it looks black because it absorbs all light that falls on its surface, like a piece of carbon. A blackbody at the temperature of absolute zero (0 K on the Kelvin scale, or −273°C) looks perfectly black, since it emits no light.

If a blackbody is heated, it becomes luminous, with a radiance and color that depend on the temperature. It looks red at about 1000 K (727°C), yellow at about 1500 K (1227°C), white at 4500 K (4227°C) and bluish-white at about 6500 K (6227°C). Further details are described in Chapter 4 and in Fig. 4.9. Figure 2.1 shows how the spectral radiance and color of a blackbody changes with the temperature, as given by the well-known blackbody radiation law. The blackbody's spectral radiance is given by

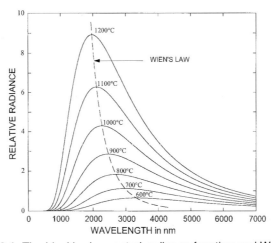

Figure 2.1 The blackbody spectral radiance function and Wien's law.

21

$$R(\lambda) = \frac{2\pi h c^2}{\lambda^5} \frac{1}{e^{ch/\lambda kT} - 1}, \tag{2.1}$$

where h is Planck's constant, k is the Boltzmann constant, c is the speed of light, λ is the wavelength, and T is the absolute temperature. The wavelength at which the peak of radiation occurs is given by Wien's displacement law, which can be derived from the blackbody radiation law

$$\lambda_m T = \frac{ch}{4.965k} = 0.0028978 \; m^0 K, \tag{2.2}$$

and it is represented by the dotted line in Fig. 2.1. Using this law, the temperature of an incandescent body, like a star or an object in an oven, can be estimated from its color.

By analogy, if a light source has a radiation peak at the wavelength λ_{max} and corresponds to temperature T on a blackbody, we say that its color temperature is T. However, this is not the real temperature unless the light source is a blackbody. In the case of an incandescent temperature lamp with a white glass bulb, the source is closer to being a blackbody than in the case of a lamp with a colored glass bulb. A fluorescent lamp is far from being a blackbody. An ordinary noncolored incandescent lamp has a color temperature of about 2850 K, while a "cool white" fluorescent lamp has a color temperature of about 4100 K.

Since it depends on many factors, daylight does not have a constant color temperature even on a clear day. Its color temperature is lower, or redder, at sunrise and sunset, and higher, or bluer, at noon.

2.3 Tungsten lamps

A tungsten lamp emits light with a high temperature by means of an incandescent filament. The radiation spectrum of a tungsten lamp can be approximated using the radiation spectrum of a blackbody. The spectral emission of a blackbody in the visible range, which is quite similar to that of the incandescent tungsten lamp, is multiplied by a constant efficiency factor.

Figure 2.2 plots the blackbody's spectral radiance for different temperatures, where each radiance function is multiplied by a proper constant so that they have the same value at a wavelength of 560 nm. As shown in this figure, the blackbody emits a white color and is almost constantly radiant in the visible interval when the temperature is about 5500 K, which is close to the sun's temperature. Thus, this temperature would give the light source the maximum luminous efficiency as defined in Sec. 1.4. However, this is not the proper temperature for a tungsten lamp because at such a high temperature the tungsten would rapidly evaporate. The luminous power efficiency is defined as the

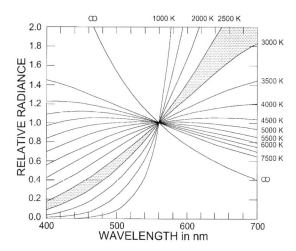

Figure 2.2 The emission spectral radiance curves of a blackbody in the visible range, normalized so that they have the same value at a wavelength of 560 nm. These curves approach those of a tungsten lamp, which operate in the range of color temperatures from 2500 K to 3000 K.

luminosity in lumens divided by the electrical power supplied to the lamp in watts. This luminous power efficiency is maximized (about 20 times) for temperatures between 2500 K and 3000 K, as shown in the shaded area in Fig. 2.2.

The spectral radiance emitted by the lamp is equal to the spectral radiance emitted by the tungsten multiplied by the spectral absorption of the glass envelope. The temperature of the filament depends on several factors, but mainly on the working voltage and the electric current. Thus, the characteristic color and the spectral radiance are dependent upon this temperature.

2.4 Gas-discharge and fluorescent lamps

A gas-discharge lamp is a glass tube with two electrodes to which an electrical current is applied. The tube contains a low-pressure gas like hydrogen, argon, neon, or a vaporized metal like mercury, whose emission spectrum is seen in Fig. 2.3. When an electrical discharge excites the gas or metal vapor, light is emitted with a spectrum formed by a series of spectral lines, which is characteristic of the gas or vapor, but unlike the continuous spectrum of an incandescent lamp. Gas-discharge lamps with mercury vapor or sodium are used for street illumination. In the mercury lamp, the vapor discharge is blue and contains much ultraviolet, which can be blocked out with the proper glass envelope if desired. A sodium lamp discharge is orange yellow. The spectrum of gas- or vapor-discharge lamps is greatly dependent on the internal pressure of the gas or vapor.

A fluorescent lamp is a mercury-vapor lamp with a fluorescent powder coating inside the surface of the glass tube. When the ultraviolet light emitted by

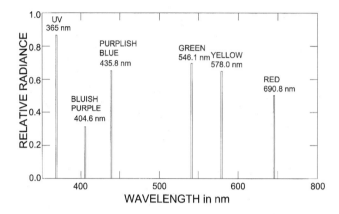

Figure 2.3 The emission spectrum of Mercury vapor.

the mercury vapor hits the fluorescent powder, this energy is converted to visible light with a continuous spectrum. The color of this emitted visible light can be chosen with the proper selection of the fluorescent powder. A white light closely resembling daylight illumination can be obtained. As shown in Fig. 2.4, the spectrum can be seen to contain a continuum due to the fluorescent powder with the discrete mercury-vapor spectral lines superimposed.

2.5 Standard light sources and illuminants

Obviously, the most important light source is natural daylight. Unfortunately, its spectral characteristics are quite variable with the time, geographic location, and the weather. Atmospheric transparency and clouds can change daylight in a few minutes. Color temperatures of daylight vary from about 2000 K in late morning to above 10,000 K in late afternoon.

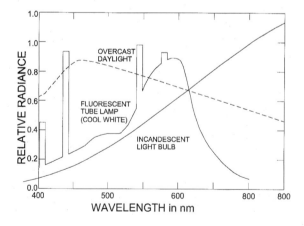

Figure 2.4 The spectrum of a cool-white fluorescent lamp (frequently called an F2 illuminant) compared to an incandescent lamp (illuminant A), and with overcast daylight illumination.

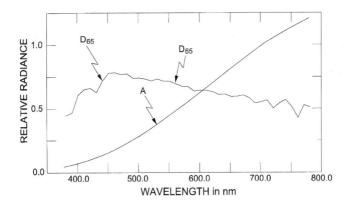

Figure 2.5 The spectral radiance of standard illuminants D_{65} and A.

Formally, standard light sources and illuminants are slightly different concepts. From a formal point of view, a standard light source exists in real life and can be physically turned on and off. On the other hand, standard illuminants are mathematical (numerical) descriptions of ideal light sources. However, some light sources are specially designed and constructed to emulate illuminants, making these terms almost equivalent for many practical purposes. In 1931, the CIE convention recommended three standard illuminants (CIE, 1932) defined by some real light sources.

Illuminant A (Fig 2.5) is formed by a gas-filled incandescent lamp with a coiled tungsten filament and a quartz bulb. Its color temperature is 2856 K and its spectral power distribution. The second illuminant, B, now discontinued, emulates noon sunlight with the spectral power distribution, as shown in Fig. 2.6. This illuminant was produced by a double liquid filter in front of light source A, as shown in Table 2.1.

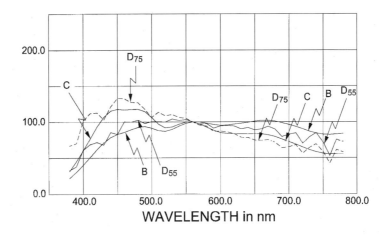

Figure 2.6 The spectral radiance of standard illuminants B, C, D_{55} and D_{75}.

Table 2.1 Liquid filters with 1-cm thickness to transform illuminant A to illuminant B.

	Components	Quantity
First filter	Copper sulfate ($CuSO_4 5H_2O$)	2.452 g
	Manita [$C_6H_8(OH)_6$]	2.452 g
	Piridina (C_5H_5N)	30.00 cm^3
	Distilled water	1000 cm^3
Second filter	Ammonium cobalt sulfate [$CoSO_4(NH_4)_2SO_4 6H_2O$]	27.71 g
	Copper sulfate ($CuSO_4 5H_2O$)	16.11 g
	Sulfuric acid (H_2SO_4) (density: 1.835)	10.00 cm^3
	Distilled water	1000 cm^3

Illuminant C, emulating average daylight, is also produced by filtering the light source emulating illuminant A with a liquid filter. However, real daylight contains more ultraviolet than illuminant C.

Due to the large fluctuations of natural daylight, illuminants B and C were considered inadequate. Instead, the CIE convention recommended a series of D illuminants with color temperatures equal to 5500 (D_{55}), 6500 (D_{65}), and 7500 (D_{75}) K, to replace illuminants B and C. As defined by the CIE Convention in 1931, the x and y chromaticity coordinates to be studied later in this book must satisfy the following relation for D illuminants:

$$2.870 \ y_D^2 - y_D - 3.000 \ x_D^2 - 0.275 = 0, \qquad (2.3)$$

with x_D in the range of 0.250 to 0.380. Here, x_D and y_D are the chromaticity coordinates to be described in Chapter 4.

The standard illuminant D_{65} represents average daylight and has a color temperature of 6500 K. Its spectral power distribution is similar to that of the discontinued illuminant C, but it has some important characteristics that make it closer to daylight. The illuminant D_{65} is based on many measurements of daylight in several countries. In graphic arts and photography, the illuminants D_{55} and D_{75} with color temperatures of 5500 K and 7500 K are sometimes used. These illuminants are obtained from the illuminant D_{65} by changing their color temperature with a procedure suggested by the CIE convention. Table 2.2 gives the relative spectral radiance of illuminants A and D_{65} calculated to 6 decimal places and in 5-nm steps.

Table 2.2 Standard Illuminants D_{65} and A.

Wave-length in nm.	A	D_{65}	Wave length in nm.	A	D_{65}
360	6.144620	46.638300	480	48.242300	115.923000
365	6.947200	49.363700	485	51.041800	112.367000
370	7.821350	52.089100	490	53.913200	108.811000
375	8.769800	51.032300	495	56.853900	109.082000
380	9.795100	49.975500	500	59.861100	109.354000
385	10.899600	52.311800	505	62.932000	108.578000
390	12.085300	54.648200	510	66.063500	107.802000
395	13.354300	68.701500	515	69.252500	106.296000
400	14.708000	82.754900	520	72.495900	104.790000
405	16.148000	87.120400	525	75.790300	106.239000
410	17.675300	91.486000	530	79.132600	107.689000
415	19.290700	92.458900	535	82.519300	106.047000
420	20.995000	93.431800	540	85.947000	104.405000
425	22.788300	90.057000	545	89.412400	104.225000
430	24.670900	86.682300	550	92.912000	104.046000
435	26.642500	95.773600	555	96.442300	102.023000
440	28.702700	104.865000	560	100.000000	100.000000
445	30.850800	110.936000	565	103.582000	98.167100
450	33.085900	117.008000	570	107.184000	96.334200
455	35.406800	117.410000	575	110.803000	96.061100
460	37.812100	117.812000	580	114.436000	95.788000
465	40.300200	116.336000	585	118.080000	92.236800
470	42.869300	114.861000	590	121.731000	88.685600
475	45.517400	115.392000	595	125.386000	89.345900

Table 2.2 Continued.

Wave-length in nm.	A	D_{65}	Wave length in nm.	A	D_{65}
600	129.04300	90.006200	720	210.36500	61.604000
605	132.69700	89.802600	725	213.26800	65.744800
610	136.34600	89.599100	730	216.12000	69.885600
615	139.98800	88.648900	735	218.92000	72.486300
620	143.61800	87.698700	740	221.66700	75.087000
625	147.23500	85.493600	745	224.36100	69.339800
630	150.83600	83.288600	750	227.00000	63.592700
635	154.41800	83.493900	755	229.58500	55.005400
640	157.97900	83.699200	760	232.11500	46.418200
645	161.51600	81.863000	765	234.58900	56.611800
650	165.02800	80.026800	770	237.00800	66.805400
655	168.51000	80.120700	775	239.37000	65.094100
660	171.96300	80.214600	780	241.67500	63.382800
665	175.38300	81.246200	785	243.92400	63.843400
670	178.76900	82.277800	790	246.11600	64.304000
675	182.11800	80.281000	795	248.25100	61.877900
680	185.42900	78.284200	800	250.32900	59.451900
685	188.70100	74.002700	805	252.35000	55.705400
690	191.93100	69.721300	810	254.31400	51.959000
695	195.11800	70.665200	815	256.22100	54.699800
700	198.26100	71.609100	820	258.07100	57.440600
705	201.35900	72.979000	825	259.86500	58.876500
710	204.40900	74.349000	830	261.602000	60.312500
715	207.41100	67.976500			

Table 2.3 Standard Illuminants B, C, D_{55} and D_{75}.

Wave-length nm	B	C	D_{55}	D_{75}	Wave-length nm	B	C	D_{55}	D_{75}
380	21.8	31.3	32.6	66.7	580	98.2	92.9	97.7	94.2
390	30.4	45.0	38.1	70.0	590	96.5	88.5	91.4	87.0
400	40.2	60.1	61.0	101.9	600	95.3	85.2	94.4	87.2
410	50.7	76.5	68.6	111.9	610	95.8	84.0	95.1	86.1
420	61.5	93.2	71.6	112.8	620	97.0	83.7	94.2	83.6
430	71.1	106.7	67.9	103.1	630	98.2	83.6	90.4	78.7
440	78.6	115.4	85.6	121.2	640	99.4	83.4	92.3	78.4
450	83.1	117.8	98.0	133.0	650	101.1	83.8	88.9	74.8
460	85.9	116.9	100.5	132.4	660	102.1	83.5	90.3	74.3
470	89.5	117.6	99.9	127.3	670	102.0	82.0	93.9	75.4
480	92.6	117.7	102.7	126.8	680	101.1	79.8	90.0	71.6
490	93.9	114.6	98.1	117.8	690	98.8	76.2	79.7	63.9
500	91.6	106.5	100.7	106.6	700	96.4	72.5	82.8	65.1
510	88.2	97.2	100.7	113.7	710	93.6	68.8	84.8	68.1
520	87.1	92.0	100.0	108.7	720	90.4	64.9	70.2	56.4
530	89.7	93.1	104.2	110.4	730	87.0	61.2	79.3	64.2
540	94.3	97.0	102.1	106.3	740	84.5	58.4	85.0	69.2
550	98.2	99.9	103.3	104.9	750	82.9	56.2	71.9	58.6
560	100.0	100.0	100.0	100.0	760	82.4	55.2	52.8	42.6
570	99.8	97.2	97.2	95.6	770	83.1	55.3	75.9	61.4

Table 2.3 gives the radiance values for the discontinued or less-used illuminants B and C, as well as for the illuminants D_{55} and D_{75} to only one decimal place and in 10-nm steps. All tabulated values for standard illuminants were normalized by multiplying them by an appropriate factor so that their value is equal to 100 for a wavelength of 560 nm. Therefore, the relative spectral irradiance values can be larger than 100 for some wavelengths.

Good daylight simulators are very important in colorimetry and color control. Many attempts have been made to simulate these illuminants, as described by McCamy (1994). The best instruments use high-pressure xenon-arc lamps with the appropriate filters. In practice, D illuminants can be approximated by several methods, for example, by a tungsten lamp and a colored bluish glass filter.

References

CIE, Commission Internationale de l'Éclairage Proceedings, 1931, Cambridge, Cambridge University Press (1932).

Eby J. E. and R. E. Levin, "Incoherent Light Sources," in *Applied Optics and Optical Engineering*, Vol. 7, Chapter 1, R. Kingslake, Ed., Academic Press, New York (1979).

Elenbaas W., *Light Sources*, Crane, Russak and Company, New York (1972).

LaRocca A., "Artificial Sources," in *Handbook of Optics*, Vol. I, Chapter 10, McGraw Hill Inc., New York (1995).

Malacara Z. and A. Morales, "Light Sources," in *Geometrical and Instrumental Optics*, Vol. 25, D. Malacara, Ed., Academic Press, Inc., New York (1988).

McCamy C. S., "Simulation of Daylight for Viewing and Measuring Color," *Color Res. Appl.*, **19**, pp. 437–445 (1994).

Chapter 3
Trichromatic Theory

3.1 Grassmann laws

The basic laws for additional colors and color-matching experiments were established by Grassmann (1853), who attributed many of his ideas to Maxwell. The laws Grassmann developed from these experiments state the following:

(a) To specify a color, three elements are necessary and sufficient: the hue, the luminance, and the luminance of the intermixed white, which defines the saturation.
(b) For every color, there is complementary color, which, when mixed, becomes a colorless gray.
(c) Two lights of different color with the same hue and saturation, when mixed, produce another color with identical hue and saturation independently of their power spectra.
(d) The total luminance of any mixture of light is the sum of each light's luminance.

These laws are the basis of all mathematical procedures established in colorimetry. However, some important conditions must be considered:

(a) All color matches must be made under similar conditions.
(b) The eye's previous exposure to light affects the state of *adaptation*, influencing the spectral sensitivity of the eye.
(c) If a field diameter larger than 10 deg is used in a color match, a failure of the proportionality law may be found.

3.2 Maxwell triangle

Probably the first attempts to produce color curves describing the trichromatic theory of color were those by Maxwell (1857, 1860). As described earlier, the first chromaticity diagram was a circle devised by Newton. Later, Maxwell used an equilateral triangle (Fig. 3.1). In his trichromatic theory, each of the three primary colors—red, green, and blue—is located at a corner of the triangle. The white color is in the middle. Other colors are formed by a combination of the r, g, b components depending on the distances from each of the three sides of the triangle. This triangular representation has been used often with several modifications. It is not clear how Maxwell defined and used it (Wintringham, 1951).

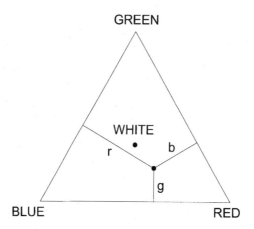

Figure 3.1 Maxwell's triangle.

3.3 Color-matching experiments

After the work by Maxwell, the next experimental work to obtain color curves was done by König (1903) with the collaboration of Dieterici. Another important work aimed at obtaining color curves was carried out by Ives (1915 and 1923) who adjusted the curves previously obtained by König, thus developing the König-Ives color-matching data. Several other researchers worked on these color-curve measurements at this time, but an important event occurred when, in 1922, the Optical Society of America (OSA) published a very extensive report by the OSA Colorimetry Committee (Troland, 1922). W. D. Wright, a leader in the field, describes the complete history of developments that eventually led to the CIE system of 1931, in an interesting appendix in the book by Boynton (1979).

To begin studying the CIE color system, let us consider the color-matching experiment in Fig. 3.2. Here, the color of two small regions on a screen with a

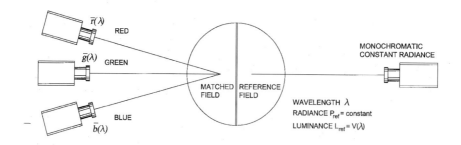

Figure 3.2 Color-matching fields with a monochromatic reference field.

split field, technically called a bipartite screen, is to be matched. The entire illuminated region subtends a visual angle of 2 deg, so that only the light receptors in the fovea at the center of the observer's retina are illuminated. One half of the field is the *reference field* illuminated with a spectrally pure monochromatic beam of light. The other half of the field is the *matched field*, whose color, as defined by its hue, purity, and luminance, is to be made equal to that of the reference field. The matched field is illuminated with the combination of three monochromatic light beams, red (700 nm), green (546.1 nm), and blue (435.8 nm). These colors correspond to three spectrum lines in mercury vapor (see Fig. 2.3).

To begin the color-matching procedure, the spectrally pure reference field is set to a wavelength of 700 nm, a red color, with any desired radiance defined as P_{Ref}. A perfect color match is achieved when the red light in the matched field, is adjusted to the same luminance as the reference field. The green and blue beam luminances are set to zero.

Then, the wavelength in the reference field is decreased in constant steps $\Delta\lambda$, preserving the same constant radiance P_{Ref} for all wavelengths, until the entire visible range is covered. Equations (1.8) and (1.9) express the relation of the luminance and radiance of an extended monochromatic light source applied to the monochromatic reference field. This can be obtained as follows:

$$L_{Ref}(\lambda) = 683\, P_{Ref}\, V(\lambda), \tag{3.1}$$

where $V(\lambda)$ is the relative photopic luminous efficiency of the eye. Since the radiance $P_{Ref}(\lambda)$ remains the same for all wavelengths, the corresponding luminance $L_{Ref}(\lambda)$ for all values of λ is directly proportional to the function $V(\lambda)$.

At every step in wavelength, the luminances $L_r(\lambda)$, $L_g(\lambda)$, and $L_b(\lambda)$, and corresponding radiances $P_r(\lambda)$, $P_g(\lambda)$, and $P_b(\lambda)$ for the red, green, and blue beams on the matched field, are adjusted by careful trial and error. The matched field and the reference field must have the same hue, saturation and luminance. In other words, they should be identical. These three luminances are related to their corresponding radiances by

$$L_r(\lambda) = 683\, P_r(\lambda)\, V(\lambda)$$

$$L_g(\lambda) = 683\, P_g(\lambda)\, V(\lambda) \tag{3.2}$$

$$L_b(\lambda) = 683\, P_b(\lambda)\, V(\lambda).$$

The total luminance of $L_{Mch}(\lambda)$ in the matched field can be expressed by the sum of the luminances of the three beams as

$$L_{Mch}(\lambda) = L_r(\lambda) + L_g(\lambda) + L_b(\lambda). \qquad (3.3)$$

Thus, from Eqs. (3.2) and (3.3) we can write

$$L_{Mch}(\lambda) = 683[P_r(\lambda)V_r + P_g(\lambda)\ V_g + P_b(\lambda)V_b]. \qquad (3.4)$$

It is important to notice that the sum of the three radiances $P_r(\lambda)$, $P_g(\lambda)$, and $P_b(\lambda)$ is the total radiance $P_{Mch}(\lambda)$ on the matched field. However, this is not equal to the radiance P_{Ref} in the reference field. Although the radiance P_{Ref} in the reference field is the same for all of the wavelengths, the radiance $P_{Mch}(\lambda)$ in the matched field has a different value for every wavelength in the visible range. Equivalently, we can say that after the matching procedure, the luminances for both the reference and the matched fields are equal but not necessarily to their radiances. This is easy to understand since the spectral distribution of the two fields is different. Thus, by equating expressions (3.1) and (3.4) and using Eq. (3.3) we can find

$$L_{Ref}(\lambda) = L_{Mch}(\lambda) =$$

$$P_{Ref}\ V(\lambda) = 683[P_r(\lambda)V_r + P_g(\lambda)\ V_g + P_b(\lambda)V_b], \qquad (3.5)$$

where each of these three terms represent the combined luminance for the red, green, and blue components of the matched field. In the same manner, we can obtain

$$P_{Ref} = \frac{1}{V(\lambda)}[P_r(\lambda)V_r + P_g(\lambda)\ V_g + P_b(\lambda)V_b], \qquad (3.6)$$

where each of these three terms represent the radiance for the red, green, and blue components of the matched field. Alternatively, we can also write

$$V(\lambda) = \frac{1}{P_{Ref}}[P_r(\lambda)V_r + P_g(\lambda)\ V_g + P_b(\lambda)V_b]. \qquad (3.7)$$

Therefore, the function $V(\lambda)$ is equal to the sum of the three terms that are directly proportional to the luminances of the three beams in the matching field. Each one of these three terms is a function of the wavelength and can be represented by the product of two numbers, a function of the wavelength λ and a constant L_R, L_G, or L_B, which are not the same as the luminance $L_r(\lambda)$, $L_g(\lambda)$, and $L_b(\lambda)$ as previously defined. Thus, we can write

$$V(\lambda) = L_R \; \overline{r}(\lambda) + L_G \; \overline{g}(\lambda) + L_B \; \overline{b}(\lambda), \tag{3.8}$$

where the stimuli values $\overline{r}(\lambda), \overline{g}(\lambda)$, and $\overline{b}(\lambda)$ are called the *color-matching functions*.

The units of these stimuli are defined by the selection of the constants L_R, L_G, and L_B. The units of $\overline{r}(\lambda)$ are defined by choosing $L_R = 1$. We now require that the sum of the measured discrete values of $\overline{r}(\lambda)$, $\overline{g}(\lambda)$, $\overline{b}(\lambda)$ be expressed as

$$\sum_{i=1}^{N} \overline{r}(\lambda_i) = \sum_{i=1}^{N} \overline{g}(\lambda_i) = \sum_{i=1}^{N} \overline{b}(\lambda_i), \tag{3.9}$$

where N is the total number of measured values in the whole spectral range. In this manner, the numerical values of L_R, L_G, L_B and the units of $\overline{r}(\lambda), \overline{g}(\lambda), \overline{b}(\lambda)$ are determined. This scaling of the tristimulus values is advantageous in that the corresponding values for white with constant energy have the same magnitudes, as will be described in the next chapter.

The relative spectral radiances per stimulus unit of each of the three components are $L_R \, \overline{r}(\lambda), L_G \, \overline{g}(\lambda) \, V_R/V_B$, and $L_B \, \overline{b}(\lambda) \, V_R/V_B$. Table 3.1 shows the values for the relative radiances and the luminances per stimulus unit.

Table 3.1 Radiances and luminances

	Wavelength in nm	Relative spectral radiance/stimulus unit	Relative spectral luminance/stimulus unit
Red	700.0	$1.0000 \, (L_R \, V_R/V_R)$	$1.0000 \, (L_R)$
Green	546.1	$0.0190 \, (L_G \, V_R/V_G)$	$4.5907 \, (L_G)$
Blue	435.8	$0.0140 \, (L_B \, V_R/V_B)$	$0.0601 \, (L_B)$

3.4 Color-matching functions $\overline{r}(\lambda), \overline{g}(\lambda), \overline{b}(\lambda)$

Let us consider the superimposition of three light fields with monochromatic colors red (700 nm), green (546.1 nm) and blue (435.8 nm), that have the relative luminances $L_R \, \overline{r}(\lambda), L_G \, \overline{g}(\lambda)$, and $L_B \, \overline{b}(\lambda)$, respectively. The resulting matched field has a relative luminance $V(\lambda)$, and the same color and luminance as the reference monochromatic light field with the wavelength λ. This monochromatic reference field has a constant radiance independent of its color (wavelength), but its radiance is not necessarily the same as that for the matched field formed by the superposition of the three colors.

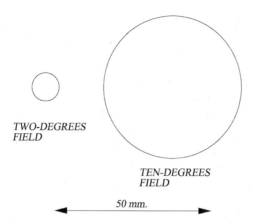

TWO-DEGREES
FIELD

TEN-DEGREES
FIELD

50 mm.

Figure 3.3 Two-deg and ten-deg fields as seen from a distance of 25 cm.

The original color-matching functions were obtained with a 2-deg field, to avoid stimulating the rods outside the fovea centralis, as defined by the Commission Internationale de l'Éclairage (CIE) convention in 1931 (CIE, 1932). These color-matching functions were obtained by reconstructing relative color-matching data previously obtained by Wright (1928-1929) and Guild (1931), and by using different experimental methods.

Wright and Guild reconstructed the color-matching functions assuming that a linear combination of these functions must be equal to the 1924 function $V(\lambda)$ by CIE [Eq. (3.8)]. This hypothesis was reasonable, since the red, green, and blue beams add up to a field with a constant radiance for all wavelengths. Unfortunately, as shown by several authors, the reconstruction of the functions was highly questionable (Sperling, 1958) because of the validity of the curve $V(\lambda)$ used in the reconstruction (Gibson and Tyndall, 1923; CIE, 1926; and Jud, 1951). This is because, as explained in Chapter 2, the function $V(\lambda)$ has a noticeable error in the blue region. Later, Jud (1951) and Vos (1978) made corrections to these functions, as discussed by Stockman and Sharpe (1999). Stiles and Burch (1955) also obtained these matching functions from direct measurements of 10 observers.

The 2-deg field is too small for many practical purposes, so a 10-deg field was adopted by the CIE convention in 1964, based on the work of Stiles and Burch (1959), and Speranskaya (1959). The color-matching functions $\bar{r}(\lambda)$, $\bar{g}(\lambda)$, and $\bar{b}(\lambda)$, for a 10-deg field were directly measured in 49 subjects from 392.2 nm to 714.3 nm, and from 714.3 to 824.2 nm in 9 subjects. During the measurements, the luminance of the matching field was kept high to reduce any effect from stimulation of the rods as much as possible. If desired, a correction for the rods intrusion can be made, as shown by Stockman and Sharpe (1999).

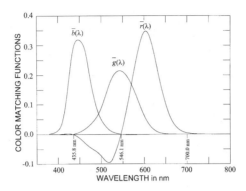

Figure 3.4 Color-matching functions $\bar{r}(\lambda)$, $\bar{g}(\lambda)$, $\bar{b}(\lambda)$ for a 2-deg field (CIE, 1931).

Color perception, mainly large-field color-matching functions, has been studied under different experimental conditions and methods (Lozano and Palmer, 1968; Burns and Elsner, 1985 and 1993; and Gordon and Abramov, 1977). Figure 3.3 shows the 2-deg and the 10-deg fields as seen from a distance of 25 cm.

In 1931, the color-matching functions were defined in the wavelength range of 380.0 nm to 780 nm at intervals of 5 nm, with their values given to five decimal places. These functions are found in Table 3.2, and plotted in Fig. 3.4.

3.5 Tristimulus values *R, G, B*

We assumed in the preceding section that the reference field was illuminated by a monochromatic beam of light with a radiance unit. Let us now assume that the reference field is illuminated by the superposition of two or more monochromatic spectral lines with wavelengths λ_1, λ_2, λ_3, etc. with radiances $P(\lambda_1)$, $P(\lambda_2)$, $P(\lambda_3)$, etc., as shown in Fig. 3.5. To match the color component with wavelength λ_1 we need the color-matching functions $\bar{r}(\lambda_1)$, $\bar{g}(\lambda_1)$, and $\bar{b}(\lambda_1)$, with a radiance of $P(\lambda_1)$. To match the color component with wavelength λ_2 we need the color-matching functions $\bar{r}(\lambda_2)$, $\bar{g}(\lambda_2)$, and $\bar{b}(\lambda_2)$ with a radiance of $P(\lambda_2)$, and so on. So, to match the field formed by two or more wavelengths we need the combined color-matching functions, called tristimulus values and expressed as $R = P(\lambda_1)\bar{r}(\lambda_1) + P(\lambda_2)\bar{r}(\lambda_2) + P(\lambda_3)\bar{r}(\lambda_3) +...$, $G = P(\lambda_1)\bar{g}(\lambda_1) + P(\lambda_2)\bar{g}(\lambda_2) + P(\lambda_3)\bar{g}(\lambda_3) +...$, and $B = P(\lambda_1)\bar{b}(\lambda_1) + P(\lambda_2)\bar{b}(\lambda_2) + P(\lambda_3)\bar{b}(\lambda_3)$. Generalizing this result for a reference field illuminated by a light source with a continuous power spectrum where the irradiance per unit wavelength interval $\Delta\lambda$ is $P(\lambda)$, the required tristimulus values to match this light field is

$$R = \int_0^\infty P(\lambda)\,\bar{r}(\lambda)\,\mathrm{d}\lambda,\qquad(3.10)$$

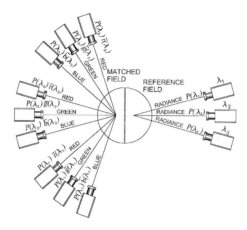

Figure 3.5 Color-matching fields with a polychromatic reference field.

$$G = \int_0^\infty P(\lambda)\, \overline{g}(\lambda)\ d\lambda\,, \tag{3.11}$$

and

$$B = \int_0^\infty P(\lambda)\, \overline{b}(\lambda)\ d\lambda\,, \tag{3.12}$$

or equivalently, for discrete values

$$R = \sum_{i=1}^{N} P(\lambda_i)\, \overline{r}(\lambda_i)\,, \tag{3.13}$$

$$G = \sum_{i=1}^{N} P(\lambda_i)\, \overline{g}(\lambda_i)\,, \tag{3.14}$$

and

$$B = \sum_{i=1}^{N} P(\lambda_i)\, \overline{b}(\lambda_i)\,. \tag{3.15}$$

If an equal energy white is such that $P(\lambda) = 1$, we can see that the values of R, G, and B are equal. The luminances for each of these three components are $L_R R$,

$L_G G$, and $L_B B$. The total luminance of the superposition is the sum of these three luminances. These three tristimulus values define the light field color with its hue, saturation, and luminance.

3.6 Chromaticity coordinates *r, g, b*

In a coordinate system with three orthogonal axes *r, g, b*, all colors with the same hue and saturation but different luminance are represented by points on a straight line passing through the origin. The distance from the origin to a point on this line is determined by its luminance.

The monochromatic spectral colors with constant radiance are represented by points with coordinates $\bar{r}(\lambda)$, $\bar{g}(\lambda)$, $\bar{b}(\lambda)$ along a curve, as shown in the stereoscopic pair of images in Fig. 3.6. This is called the Schrödinger (1920) spectrum bag. Notice that this curve is not completely inside the cube because some values of the color-matching functions are negative.

All points on this curve can be projected to a plane $r + g + b = 1$ that intersects at the coordinate axes at the points (1,0,0), (0,1,0), and (0,0,1). The points on this projected curve have coordinates $r(\lambda)$, $g(\lambda)$, $b(\lambda)$, given by

$$r(\lambda) = \frac{\bar{r}(\lambda)}{\bar{r}(\lambda) + \bar{g}(\lambda) + \bar{b}(\lambda)}, \qquad (3.16)$$

$$g(\lambda) = \frac{\bar{g}(\lambda)}{\bar{r}(\lambda) + \bar{g}(\lambda) + \bar{b}(\lambda)}, \qquad (3.17)$$

and

$$b(\lambda) = \frac{\bar{b}(\lambda)}{\bar{r}(\lambda) + \bar{g}(\lambda) + \bar{b}(\lambda)}, \qquad (3.18)$$

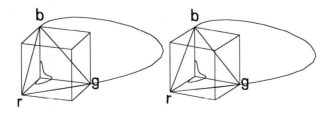

Figure 3.6 A stereo pair showing the color-matching functions in $\bar{r}(\lambda), \bar{g}(\lambda), \bar{b}(\lambda)$ in $\bar{r}, \bar{g}, \bar{b}$ space, and the projection of the color matching functions to obtain the chromaticity coordinates.

with the following relation between them:

$$r(\lambda) + g(\lambda) + b(\lambda) = 1.\tag{3.19}$$

In Fig. 3.6, this relationship is represented by a large loop resembling a fragment of an ellipse, with all points lying in the inclined plane passing through the unit vectors. After this transformation, the projection of the points along the projected curve for the spectrally pure monochromatic colors will not have constant power, nor will they have constant luminosity. The points on the plane represented by this expression can now be projected to the plane r, g, by making the coordinate b equal to zero. Then, just two coordinate values called *chromaticity coordinates*, as plotted in Fig. 3.7, are sufficient to represent any color with its hue and saturation. However, with this representation of a plane, all information about the luminance is lost. The locus of all spectrally pure colors is obtained by plotting the values of $\bar{r}(\lambda)$ versus $\bar{g}(\lambda)$, as in Fig. 3.8. The values r, g, b defining the hue and saturation of any color are the chromaticity coordinates, which can be obtained by normalizing the tristimulus values, as follows:

$$r = \frac{R}{R+G+B},\tag{3.20}$$

$$g = \frac{G}{R+G+B},\tag{3.21}$$

and

$$b = \frac{B}{R+G+B},\tag{3.22}$$

where

$$r + g + b = 1.\tag{3.23}$$

The values of the chromaticity coordinates $r(\lambda)$, $g(\lambda)$, $b(\lambda)$ for spectrally pure colors, and for a 2-deg field as defined by the CIE convention in 1931, are in Table 3.3.

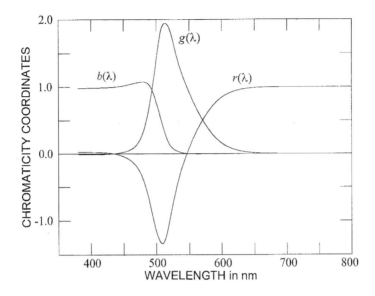

Figure 3.7 Chromaticity coordinates $r(\lambda)$, $g(\lambda)$, $b(\lambda)$ for spectrally pure colors for a 2-deg field (CIE, 1931).

Table 3.2 Color-matching functions $\bar{r}(\lambda)$, $\bar{g}(\lambda)$, $\bar{b}(\lambda)$ for a 2-deg field (CIE, 1931).

Wave-length in nm.	$\bar{r}(\lambda)$	$\bar{g}(\lambda)$	$\bar{b}(\lambda)$	Wave-length in nm.	$\bar{r}(\lambda)$	$\bar{g}(\lambda)$	$\bar{b}(\lambda)$
380	0.00003	−0.00001	0.00117	450	−0.01213	0.00678	0.31670
385	0.00005	−0.00002	0.00189	455	−0.01874	0.01046	0.31166
390	0.00010	−0.00004	0.00359	460	−0.02608	0.01485	0.29821
395	0.00017	−0.00007	0.00647	465	−0.03324	0.01977	0.27295
400	0.00030	−0.00014	0.01214	470	−0.03933	0.02538	0.22991
405	0.00047	−0.00022	0.01969	475	−0.04471	0.03183	0.18592
410	0.00084	−0.00041	0.03707	480	−0.04939	0.03914	0.14494
415	0.00139	−0.00070	0.06637	485	−0.05364	0.04713	0.10968
420	0.00211	−0.00110	0.11541	490	−0.05814	0.05689	0.08257
425	0.00266	0.00143	0.18575	495	0.06414	0.06948	0.06246
430	0.00218	−0.00119	0.24769	500	−0.07173	0.08536	0.04776
435	0.00036	−0.00021	0.29012	505	−0.08120	0.10593	0.03688
440	−0.00261	0.00149	0.31228	510	−0.08901	0.12860	0.02698
445	−0.00673	0.00379	0.31860	515	−0.09356	0.15262	0.01842

Table 3.2 Continued.

Wave-length in nm.	$\overline{r}(\lambda)$	$\overline{g}(\lambda)$	$\overline{b}(\lambda)$	Wave-length in nm.	$\overline{r}(\lambda)$	$\overline{g}(\lambda)$	$\overline{b}(\lambda)$
520	−0.09264	0.17468	0.01221	655	0.07857	0.00066	−0.00001
525	−0.08473	0.19113	0.00830	660	0.05932	0.00037	0.00000
530	−0.07101	0.20317	0.00549	665	0.04366	0.00021	0.00000
535	−0.05316	0.21083	0.00320	670	0.03149	0.00011	0.00000
540	−0.03152	0.21466	0.00146	675	0.02294	0.00006	0.00000
545	−0.00613	0.21487	0.00023	680	0.01687	0.00003	0.00000
550	0.02279	0.21178	−0.00058	685	0.01187	0.00001	0.00000
555	0.05514	0.20588	−0.00105	690	0.00819	0.00000	0.00000
560	0.09060	0.19702	−0.00130	695	0.00572	0.00000	0.00000
565	0.12840	0.18522	−0.00138	700	0.00410	0.00000	0.00000
570	0.16768	0.17087	−0.00135	705	0.00291	0.00000	0.00000
575	0.20715	0.15429	−0.00123	710	0.00210	0.00000	0.00000
580	0.24526	0.13610	−0.00108	715	0.00148	0.00000	0.00000
585	0.27989	0.11686	−0.00093	720	0.00105	0.00000	0.00000
590	0.30928	0.09754	−0.00079	725	0.00074	0.00000	0.00000
595	0.33184	0.07909	−0.00063	730	0.00052	0.00000	0.00000
600	0.34429	0.06246	−0.00049	735	0.00036	0.00000	0.00000
605	0.34756	0.04776	−0.00038	740	0.00025	0.00000	0.00000
610	0.33971	0.03557	−0.00030	745	0.00017	0.00000	0.00000
615	0.32265	0.02583	−0.00022	750	0.00012	0.00000	0.00000
620	0.29708	0.01828	−0.00015	755	0.00008	0.00000	0.00000
625	0.26348	0.01253	−0.00011	760	0.00006	0.00000	0.00000
630	0.22677	0.00833	−0.00008	765	0.00004	0.00000	0.00000
635	0.19233	0.00537	−0.00005	770	0.00003	0.00000	0.00000
640	0.15968	0.00334	−0.00003	775	0.00001	0.00000	0.00000
645	0.12905	0.00199	−0.00002	780	0.00000	0.00000	0.00000
650	0.10167	0.00116	−0.00001				

It must be pointed out that these are not the only conditions that can be used in defining this transformation of units. Alternatively, instead of making the sum of the luminosities of the color-matching functions equal to that of the equal power white, as required by Eq. (3.8), they can also be made equal to the luminosity of the National Physical Laboratories (NPL), England, white (Guild,

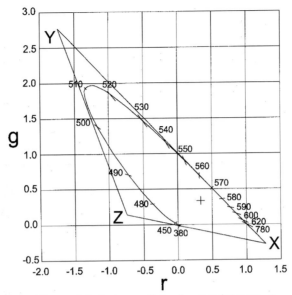

Figure 3.8 A chromaticity diagram for *r* vs. *g*.

1931). The NPL white is given by an incandescent lamp with a color temperature of about 4800 K. Wright also introduced another method to define the units of his primary stimuli (1928–1929). This method of fixing the units has some advantages and it is known as the *W. D. W. method*, after Wright.

The luminosities in the *r*, *g*, *b* space can be found using Eq. (3.8). There is a plane in the space where the luminance is zero, given by

$$L_R r + L_G g + L_B b = 0 . \tag{3.24}$$

This zero luminance plane is called the *alychne,* and it passes through the origin of coordinates of the *r*, *g*, *b* system. The normal vector to this plane bias the components L_R, L_G, and L_B. The intersection of this plane and the plane defined by Eq. (3.23) is a straight line. Therefore, the projection of this line on the *r*, *g* plane (Fig. 3.8) is another straight line given by

$$(L_R - L_B)r + (L_G - L_B)g + L_B = 0 . \tag{3.25}$$

This straight line indicates the location of purple colors.

Table 3.3 Chromaticity coordinates $r(\lambda)$, $g(\lambda)$, $b(\lambda)$ for spectrally pure colors and for a 2-deg field (CIE, 1931).

Wave-length in nm.	r(λ)	g(λ)	b(λ)	Wave-length in nm.	r(λ)	g(λ)	b(λ)
380	0.0272	−0.0115	0.9843	515	−1.2076	1.9699	0.2377
385	0.0268	−0.0114	0.9846	520	−0.9830	1.8534	0.1296
390	0.0263	−0.0114	0.9851	525	−0.7386	1.6662	0.0724
395	0.0256	−0.0113	0.9857	530	−0.5159	1.4761	0.0398
400	0.0247	−0.0112	0.9865	535	−0.3304	1.3105	0.0199
405	0.0237	−0.0111	0.9874	540	−0.1707	1.1628	0.0079
410	0.0225	−0.0109	0.9884	545	−0.0293	1.0282	0.0011
415	0.0207	−0.0104	0.9897	550	0.0974	0.9051	−0.0025
420	0.0181	−0.0094	0.9913	555	0.2121	0.7919	−0.0040
425	0.0142	−0.0076	0.9934	560	0.3164	0.6881	−0.0045
430	0.0088	−0.0048	0.9960	565	0.4112	0.5932	−0.0044
435	0.0012	−0.0007	0.9995	570	0.4973	0.5067	−0.0040
440	−0.0084	0.0048	1.0036	575	0.5751	0.4283	−0.0034
445	−0.0213	0.0120	1.0093	580	0.6449	0.3579	−0.0028
450	−0.0390	0.0218	1.0172	585	0.7071	0.2952	−0.0023
455	−0.0618	0.0345	1.0273	590	0.7617	0.2402	−0.0019
460	−0.0909	0.0517	1.0392	595	0.8087	0.1928	−0.0015
465	−0.1281	0.0762	1.0519	600	0.8475	0.1537	−0.0012
470	−0.1821	0.1175	1.0646	605	0.8800	0.1209	−0.0009
475	−0.2584	0.1840	1.0744	610	0.9059	0.0949	−0.0008
480	−0.3667	0.2906	1.0761	615	0.9265	0.0741	−0.0006
485	−0.5200	0.4568	1.0632	620	0.9425	0.0580	−0.0005
490	−0.7150	0.6996	1.0154	625	0.9550	0.0454	−0.0004
495	−0.9459	1.0247	0.9212	630	0.9649	0.0354	−0.0003
500	−1.1685	1.3905	0.7780	635	0.9730	0.0272	−0.0002
505	−1.3182	1.7195	0.5987	640	0.9797	0.0205	0.0002
510	−1.3371	1.9318	0.4053	645	0.9850	0.0152	0.0002

Table 3.3 Continued.

650	0.9888	0.0113	0.0001	720	1.0000	0.0000	0.0000
655	0.9918	0.0083	0.0001	725	1.0000	0.0000	0.0000
660	0.9940	0.0061	0.0001	730	1.0000	0.0000	0.0000
665	0.9954	0.0047	0.0001	735	1.0000	0.0000	0.0000
670	0.9966	0.0035	0.0001	740	1.0000	0.0000	0.0000
675	0.9975	0.0025	0.0000	745	1.0000	0.0000	0.0000
680	0.9984	0.0016	0.0000	750	1.0000	0.0000	0.0000
685	0.9991	0.0009	0.0000	755	1.0000	0.0000	0.0000
690	0.9996	0.0004	0.0000	760	1.0000	0.0000	0.0000
695	0.9999	0.0001	0.0000	765	1.0000	0.0000	0.0000
700	1.0000	0.0000	0.0000	770	1.0000	0.0000	0.0000
705	1.0000	0.0000	0.0000	775	1.0000	0.0000	0.0000
710	1.0000	0.0000	0.0000	780	1.0000	0.0000	0.0000
715	1.0000	0.0000	0.0000				

References

Boynton R. M., *Human Color Vision*, New York: Holt, Rinehart and Winston, (1979).

Burns S. A. and A. E. Elsner, "Color Matching at High Illuminances: The Color-Match-Area Effect and Photopigment Bleaching," *J. Opt. Soc. Am. A,* **2,** pp. 698–704 (1985).

Burns S. A. and A. E. Elsner, "Color Matching at High Illuminances: Photopigment Optical Density and Pupil Entry," *J. Opt. Soc. Am. A,* **10,** pp. 221–230 (1993).

CIE, Commission Internationale de l'Éclairage Proceedings, 1924, Cambridge, Cambridge University Press (1926).

CIE, Commission Internationale de l'Éclairage Proceedings, 1931, Cambridge, Cambridge University Press (1932).

Gibson K. S. and Tyndall, E. P. T., "Visibility of Radiant Energy," *Sc. Papers of the Bureau of Standards,* **19**, pp. 131–191 (1923).

Gordon J. and I. Abramov, "Color Vision in the Peripheral Retina. II. Hue and Saturation," *J. Opt. Soc. Am.,* **67,** pp. 202–207 (1977).

Grassmann H. G., "Theory of Compound Colors," *Annalen der Physik und Chemie,* **19**, pp. 53–60 (1853). Translation published in *Philosophical Magazine,* **4**, pp. 254–264 (1854). Reprinted in *Selected Papers in Colorimetry—Fundamentals,* D. L. MacAdam, Editor, SPIE Milestone Series, Volume MS77, (1993).

Guild J. "The Colorimetric Properties of the Spectrum," *Philos. Trans. of the Roy. Soc. of London,* **A230,** pp. 149–187 (1931).

Ives F. E., "The Transformation of Color-Mixture Equations from One System to Another,"*J. Franklin Inst.*, **180**, pp. 673 (1915).

Ives F. E., "The Transformation of Color-Mixture Equations from One System to Another II. Graphical Aids," *J. Franklin Inst.*, **195**, pp. 23 (1923).

Judd, D. B. "Report of U.S. Secretariat Committee on Colorimetry and Artificial Daylight," *Proc. of the Twelfth Session of the CIE,* **1**, pp. 11, Paris: Bureau Central de la CIE (1951).

König A. *Gesammelte Abhandlungen Zur Physiolgischen Optik*, Barth, (1903).
Lozano R. D. and D. Palmer, "Large-Field Color Matching and Adaptation," *J. Opt. Soc. Am.,* **58**, pp. 1653–1656 (1968).

Maxwell J. C., "The Diagram of Colors,"*Phil. Trans. Roy. Soc. of Edinbugh,* **21**, 275–298 (1857). Reprinted in *Selected Papers in Colorimetry—Fundamentals,* D. L. MacAdam, Editor, SPIE Milestone Series, Volume MS77, (1993).

Maxwell J. C., "On the Theory of Compound Colours and the Relations of the Colours of the Spectrum," *Proc. Roy. Soc. London,* **10**, pp. 404–409 (1860). Reprinted in *Selected Papers in Colorimetry—Fundamentals,* D. L. MacAdam, Editor, SPIE Milestone Series, Volume MS77, (1993).

Schrödinger E., "Outline of Color Measurement for Daylight Vision," *Annalen der Physik,* **63**, pp. 397–447 (1920). Reprinted in *Selected Papers in Colorimetry—Fundamentals,* D. L. MacAdam, Editor, SPIE Milestone Series, Volume MS77, (1993).

Speranskaya N. I., "Determination of Spectrum Color Co-Ordinates for Twenty-Seven Normal Observers," *Optics and Spectroscopy,* **7**, pp. 424–428 (1959).

Sperling H. G., "An Experimental Investigation of the Relationship Between Colour Mixture and Luminous Efficiency," in *Visual Problems of Colour*, Vol. 1, pp. 249–277, Her Majesty Stationery Office, London, (1958).

Stiles, W. S. and J. M. Burch, "Interim Report to the Commission Internationale de l'Eclairage Zurich, 1955, on the National Physical Laboratory's Investigation of Colour-Matching,"*Optica Acta*, **2**, pp. 168–181 (1955).

Stiles, W. S., and J. M. Burch, "NPL Colour-Matching Investigation: Final Report (1958)," *Optica Acta*, **6**, pp. 1–26 (1959).

Stockman A., and L. T. Sharpe, "Cone Spectral Sensitivities and Color Matching," *Color Vision: From Genes to Perception,* K. Gegenfurtner and L. T. Sharpe, Eds., pp. 51–85 (1999).

Troland L. T., "Report of Committee on Colorimetry for 1920–21," *J. Opt. Soc. Am.*, **6**, pp. 527–596 (1922).

Vos J. J., "Colorimetric and Photometric Properties of a 2-deg Fundamental Observer,"*Color Research and Application,* **3**, pp. 125–128 (1978).

Wright, W. D. "A Re-determination of the Trichromatic Coefficients of the Spectral Colours," *Transactions of the Optical Society*, **30**, pp. 141–164 (1928–29).

Wintringham W. T., "Color Television and Colorimetry,"*Proceedings of the IRE*, **39**, pp. 1135–1172 (1951).

Chapter 4
CIE Color Specification System

4.1 The CIE color system

A practical problem appears in the procedure to find the color-matching functions described in Chapter 3. For some wavelengths of the monochromatic reference, after decreasing the luminance of the red beam in the matched zone to zero, the color may still look too red. The only solution to have a perfect match is to add red to the reference zone, instead of taking it out of the sample—which is impossible. Mathematically, this is considered to be subtracting red light from the sample, which means that the color-matching function value is negative.

A set of three stimuli—X, Y, and Z—is defined by a linear combination of the red, green, and blue stimuli, with some of their values being negative. This transformation is accomplished by means of a projective transformation (Ives 1915, 1923), converting the system of coordinates (r, g, b) into a new system of coordinates (x, y, z). The curve of spectrally pure colors $\bar{r}(\lambda)$, $\bar{g}(\lambda)$, $\bar{b}(\lambda)$ is transformed into a curve of spectrally pure colors as defined by $\bar{x}(\lambda)$, $\bar{y}(\lambda)$, $\bar{z}(\lambda)$.

$$
\begin{bmatrix} x \\ y \\ z \end{bmatrix} = \begin{bmatrix} r_x & r_y & r_z \\ g_x & g_y & g_z \\ b_x & b_y & b_z \end{bmatrix}^{-1} \bullet \begin{bmatrix} r \\ g \\ b \end{bmatrix},
\tag{4.1}
$$

where (r_x, g_x, b_x) are the coordinates of the point $(x = 1, y = 0, z = 0)$, (r_y, g_y, b_y) are the coordinates of the point $(x = 0, y = 1, z = 0)$, and (r_z, g_z, b_z) are the coordinates of the point $(x = 0, y = 0, z = 1)$, as measured in the r, g, b system.

Let us now assume that the inverse of this matrix is A, so that we can write

$$
\begin{bmatrix} x \\ y \\ z \end{bmatrix} = \begin{bmatrix} a_{11} & a_{12} & a_{13} \\ a_{21} & a_{22} & a_{23} \\ a_{31} & a_{32} & a_{33} \end{bmatrix} \bullet \begin{bmatrix} r \\ g \\ b \end{bmatrix}.
\tag{4.2}
$$

The value of the coefficients is determined by the type of linear transformation being made.

4.2 Color-matching functions $\bar{x}(\lambda)$, $\bar{y}(\lambda)$, $\bar{z}(\lambda)$

To find the color-matching functions, we must specify several criteria to find the values for the elements of the transformation matrix. Out of practicality and convenience, it was decided that the function $\bar{y}(\lambda)$ should be equal to the luminosity function $V(\lambda)$ of the eye. So, from Eq. (3.8), the values of the matrix coefficients of the second row are $a_{21} = L_R = 1$, $a_{22} = L_G = 4.5907$, and $a_{23} = L_B = 0.0601$. Then, any color on the y-axis has zero relative spectral luminance. In other words, the *alychne* is the y-axis, with the value of $\bar{y}(\lambda)$ equal to the spectral luminous efficiency or luminosity function of the eye,

$$\bar{y}(\lambda) = V(\lambda). \tag{4.3}$$

The second criterion is that the constant energy of white, defined by $P(\lambda) = 1$, should have equal values for the three tristimuli. Thus, the three sums of all the values for different values of λ of the three color-matching functions $\bar{x}(\lambda)$, $\bar{y}(\lambda)$, and $\bar{z}(\lambda)$ should be equal. If we take the three sums of all the values of the three color-matching functions $\bar{r}(\lambda)$, $\bar{g}(\lambda)$, and $\bar{b}(\lambda)$, from Eq. (3.7) as equal to a quantity S, we have

$$\sum_{i=1}^{N}\bar{x}(\lambda_i) = S\,(a_{11} + a_{12} + a_{13}) =$$

$$\sum_{i=1}^{N}\bar{y}(\lambda_i) = S\,(a_{21} + a_{22} + a_{23}) = \tag{4.4}$$

$$\sum_{i=1}^{N}\bar{z}(\lambda_i) = S\,(a_{31} + a_{32} + a_{33}),$$

which gives us

$$(a_{11} + a_{12} + a_{13}) = (a_{21} + a_{22} + a_{23}) = (a_{31} + a_{32} + a_{33}) = \sigma. \tag{4.5}$$

The value of σ is known, since the three coefficients for the second row of the matrix have already been determined.

The third criterion is that the line joining point X with point Y in Fig. 3.8 be tangent to the curve on the red side. A practical advantage is that for these colors, a linear combination of tristimuli X and Y are sufficient to describe them, without any tristimulus Z. For the red-color point with a wavelength equal to 700 nm, we have $r = \bar{r}(\lambda) = 1$, $g = \bar{g}(\lambda) = 0$, and $b = \bar{b}(\lambda) = 0$. The line joining the points X and Y pass through this last point N at the red end of the spectrum if $a_{31} = 0$, making $\bar{z}_N(\lambda) = 0$ for any values of a_{32} and a_{33}. If we want the line X-Y to be tangent to the curve, we also require that for another point close to the endpoint, for example, the $N-1$ point,

$$\bar{z}_{N-1} = a_{32}\,\bar{g}_{N-1} + a_{33}\,\bar{b}_{N-1} = 0, \tag{4.6}$$

which gives

$$\frac{a_{33}}{a_{32}} = - \frac{\overline{g}_{N-1}}{\overline{b}_{N-1}}. \tag{4.7}$$

Thus, using Eq. (4.5) with $a_{31} = 0$ and this expression we find

$$a_{32} = \frac{\sigma}{1 - \dfrac{\overline{g}_{N-1}}{\overline{b}_{N-1}}}, \tag{4.8}$$

and

$$a_{33} = -a_{32} \frac{\overline{g}_{N-1}}{\overline{b}_{N-1}}. \tag{4.9}$$

The fourth criterion is that the $\overline{y}$-axis must be tangent to the curve, so that no value of $\overline{x}(\lambda)$ is negative. We have

$$\overline{x}_{\lambda} = a_{11}\overline{r}_{\lambda} + a_{12}\overline{g}_{\lambda} + a_{13}\overline{b}_{\lambda}, \tag{4.10}$$

and this function has a minimum that can be pushed down or pulled up by changing the value of the coefficient a_{11}. The sum of the three coefficients is equal to σ, so that we have two degrees of freedom that can be used to make the minimum of $\overline{x}(\lambda)$ equal to zero, and move the minimum position laterally. A location for this minimum is chosen so that the area of the triangle X, Y, Z, in Fig. 3.8 has the minimum area.

Finally, using these results, the following transformation is obtained:

$$\begin{bmatrix} x \\ y \\ z \end{bmatrix} = \begin{bmatrix} 2.76888 & 1.75175 & 1.13016 \\ 1 & 4.59070 & 0.06010 \\ 0 & 0.05651 & 5.59427 \end{bmatrix} \begin{bmatrix} r \\ g \\ b \end{bmatrix}, \tag{4.11}$$

or in terms of L_R, L_G, and L_B,

$$\begin{bmatrix} x \\ y \\ z \end{bmatrix} = \begin{bmatrix} 2.76888 \ L_R & 0.38159 \ L_G & 18.801 \ L_B \\ L_R & L_G & L_B \\ 0 & 0.012307 & 93.066 \ L_B \end{bmatrix} \begin{bmatrix} r \\ g \\ b \end{bmatrix}, \tag{4.12}$$

with an inverse transformation given by

$$\begin{bmatrix} r \\ g \\ b \end{bmatrix} = \begin{bmatrix} 0.41846 & -0.15860 & -0.08283 \\ -0.09117 & 0.25243 & 0.01571 \\ 0.00092 & -0.00255 & 0.17860 \end{bmatrix} \begin{bmatrix} x \\ y \\ z \end{bmatrix}. \qquad (4.13)$$

We see that the coordinate values r, g, b, corresponding to the three points in the x, y, z space $(x = 1, y = 0, z = 0)$, $(x = 0, y = 1, z = 0)$, $(x = 0, y = 0, z = 1)$, are as expressed in Table 4.1. As expected, we can notice that some required amounts of r, g, or b to obtain these points are negative.

Table 4.1 Coordinate values in the r, g, b space for each of the three unit points on the x, y, and z axes, for a 2-deg field.

Point (x, y, z)	r	g	b
(1, 0, 0)	0.41846	− 0.09117	0.00092
(0, 1, 0)	− 0.15860	0.25243	− 0.00255
(0, 0, 1)	− 0.08283	0.01571	0.17860

These color-matching functions are for a 2-deg field, so that any participation of rod vision in the measurements is avoided, as defined by the CIE (1932) convention of 1931. However, these results remain valid for field sizes from 1- to 4-deg angular subtense. These functions were defined in a wavelength range from 380 nm to 780 nm at wavelength intervals of 5 nm. In 1971, the CIE recommended a new extended set of values to redefine the 1931 standard colorimetric observer. This new table contained interpolated values at 1-nm intervals with an extended range from 360 nm to 830 nm. Table 4.2 shows these values to six decimal places, at 5-nm intervals, which are plotted in Fig. 4.1.

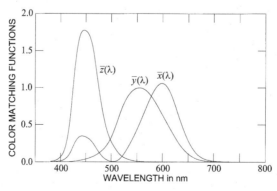

Figure 4.1 Color-matching functions $\bar{x}(\lambda)$, $\bar{y}(\lambda)$, and $\bar{z}(\lambda)$ for a 2-deg field (CIE 1931).

Table 4.2 Color-matching functions $\bar{x}(\lambda)$, $\bar{y}(\lambda)$, and $\bar{z}(\lambda)$ for a 2-deg field (CIE, 1931).

Wave-length in nm.	$\bar{x}(\lambda)$	$\bar{y}(\lambda)$	$\bar{z}(\lambda)$	Wave-length in nm.	$\bar{x}(\lambda)$	$\bar{y}(\lambda)$	$\bar{z}(\lambda)$
360	0.000130	0.000004	0.000606	515	0.029100	0.608200	0.111700
365	0.000232	0.000007	0.001086	520	0.063270	0.710000	0.078250
370	0.000415	0.000012	0.001946	525	0.109600	0.793200	0.057250
375	0.000742	0.000022	0.003486	530	0.165500	0.862000	0.042160
380	0.001368	0.000039	0.006450	535	0.225750	0.914850	0.029840
385	0.002236	0.000064	0.010550	540	0.290400	0.954000	0.020300
390	0.004243	0.000120	0.020050	545	0.359700	0.980300	0.013400
395	0.007650	0.000217	0.036210	550	0.433450	0.994950	0.008750
400	0.014310	0.000396	0.067850	555	0.512050	1.000000	0.005750
405	0.023190	0.000640	0.110200	560	0.594500	0.995000	0.003900
410	0.043510	0.001210	0.207400	565	0.678400	0.978600	0.002750
415	0.077630	0.002180	0.371300	570	0.762100	0.952000	0.002100
420	0.134380	0.004000	0.645600	575	0.842500	0.915400	0.001800
425	0.214770	0.007300	1.039050	580	0.916300	0.870000	0.001650
430	0.283900	0.011600	1.385600	585	0.978600	0.816300	0.001400
435	0.328500	0.016840	1.622960	590	1.026300	0.757000	0.001100
440	0.348280	0.023000	1.747060	595	1.056700	0.694900	0.001000
445	0.348060	0.029800	1.782600	600	1.062200	0.631000	0.000800
450	0.336200	0.038000	1.772110	605	1.045600	0.566800	0.000600
455	0.318700	0.048000	1.744100	610	1.002600	0.503000	0.000340
460	0.290800	0.060000	1.669200	615	0.938400	0.441200	0.000240
465	0.251100	0.073900	1.528100	620	0.854450	0.381000	0.000190
470	0.195360	0.090980	1.287640	625	0.751400	0.321000	0.000100
475	0.142100	0.112600	1.041900	630	0.642400	0.265000	0.000050
480	0.095640	0.139020	0.812950	635	0.541900	0.217000	0.000030
485	0.057950	0.169300	0.616200	640	0.447900	0.175000	0.000020
490	0.032010	0.208020	0.465180	645	0.360800	0.138200	0.000010
495	0.014700	0.258600	0.353300	650	0.283500	0.107000	0.000000
500	0.004900	0.323000	0.272000	655	0.218700	0.081600	0.000000
505	0.002400	0.407300	0.212300	660	0.164900	0.061000	0.000000
510	0.009300	0.503000	0.158200	665	0.121200	0.044580	0.000000

Table 4.2 Continued.

Wave-length in nm	$\bar{x}(\lambda)$	$\bar{y}(\lambda)$	$\bar{z}(\lambda)$	Wave-length in nm	$\bar{x}(\lambda)$	$\bar{y}(\lambda)$	$\bar{z}(\lambda)$
670	0.087400	0.032000	0.000000	755	0.000235	0.000085	0.000000
675	0.063600	0.023200	0.000000	760	0.000166	0.000060	0.000000
680	0.046770	0.017000	0.000000	765	0.000117	0.000042	0.000000
685	0.032900	0.011920	0.000000	770	0.000083	0.000030	0.000000
690	0.022700	0.008210	0.000000	775	0.000059	0.000021	0.000000
695	0.015840	0.005723	0.000000	780	0.000041	0.000015	0.000000
700	0.011359	0.004102	0.000000	785	0.000029	0.000011	0.000000
705	0.008111	0.002929	0.000000	790	0.000021	0.000007	0.000000
710	0.005790	0.002091	0.000000	795	0.000015	0.000005	0.000000
715	0.004106	0.001484	0.000000	800	0.000010	0.000004	0.000000
720	0.002899	0.001047	0.000000	805	0.000007	0.000003	0.000000
725	0.002049	0.000740	0.000000	810	0.000005	0.000002	0.000000
730	0.001440	0.000520	0.000000	815	0.000004	0.000001	0.000000
735	0.001000	0.000361	0.000000	820	0.000002	0.000001	0.000000
740	0.000690	0.000249	0.000000	825	0.000002	0.000001	0.000000
745	0.000476	0.000172	0.000000	830	0.000001	0.000000	0.000000
750	0.000332	0.000120	0.000000				

Another slightly different set of color-matching functions was recommended by the CIE in 1964, which is more accurate for fields larger than 4 deg. These functions were measured for a field of 10 deg. These functions, defined in a wavelength range of 360 nm to 830 nm, are plotted in Fig. 4.2 and tabulated in Table 4.3. The precision of the larger field functions is generally considered more satisfactory for most practical applications. The difference between a large and a small field is clearly observed in a very large uniform field, where its appearance to the observer shows a central spot with a slightly different color. This central zone is known as the Maxwell spot, which has a diameter of about 4 deg. When the eye looks to a different point, the Maxwell spot moves with the eye. This spot is more visible with a moderate luminance of the field. This is due to the presence of the macular pigment in the central portion of the retina.

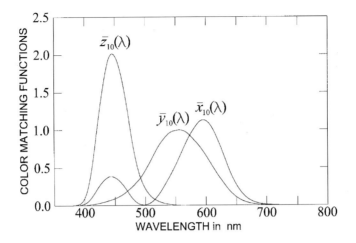

Figure 4.2 Color-matching functions $\bar{x}_{10}(\lambda), \bar{y}_{10}(\lambda),$ and $\bar{z}_{10}(\lambda)$ for a 10-deg field (CIE 1964).

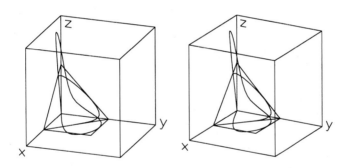

Figure 4.3 A stereo-image pair representing the color-matching functions in x, y, z space and projected to an $x + y + z = 1$ plane.

It is interesting to notice that the spectral relative luminous efficiency of the eye $V(\lambda)$ is not defined for large fields, but only for a 3-deg field. Then, $\bar{y}_{10}(\lambda)$ is slightly different from $V(\lambda)$, with the most noticeable difference found in the blue region.

The color-matching functions in the x, y, z space are represented in the stereoscopic image pair in Fig. 4.3.

Table 4.3 Color-matching functions $\bar{x}_{10}(\lambda)$, $\bar{y}_{10}(\lambda)$, and $\bar{z}_{10}(\lambda)$ for a 10-deg field (CIE, 1964).

Wave-length in nm.	$\bar{x}_{10}(\lambda)$	$\bar{y}_{10}(\lambda)$	$\bar{z}_{10}(\lambda)$	Wave-length in nm.	$\bar{x}_{10}(\lambda)$	$\bar{y}_{10}(\lambda)$	$\bar{z}_{10}(\lambda)$
360	0.000000	0.000000	0.000001	520	0.117749	0.761757	0.060709
365	0.000001	0.000000	0.000004	525	0.172953	0.823330	0.043050
370	0.000006	0.000001	0.000026	530	0.236491	0.875211	0.030451
375	0.000033	0.000004	0.000146	535	0.304213	0.923810	0.020584
380	0.000160	0.000017	0.000705	540	0.376772	0.961988	0.013676
385	0.000662	0.000072	0.002928	545	0.451584	0.982200	0.007918
390	0.002362	0.000253	0.010482	550	0.529826	0.991761	0.003988
395	0.007242	0.000768	0.032344	555	0.616053	0.999110	0.001091
400	0.019110	0.002004	0.086011	560	0.705224	0.997340	0.000000
405	0.043400	0.004509	0.197120	565	0.793832	0.982380	0.000000
410	0.084736	0.008756	0.389366	570	0.878655	0.955552	0.000000
415	0.140638	0.014456	0.656760	575	0.951162	0.915175	0.000000
420	0.204492	0.021391	0.972542	580	1.014160	0.868934	0.000000
425	0.264737	0.029497	1.282500	585	1.074300	0.825623	0.000000
430	0.314679	0.038676	1.553480	590	1.118520	0.777405	0.000000
435	0.357719	0.049602	1.798500	595	1.134300	0.720353	0.000000
440	0.383734	0.062077	1.967280	600	1.123990	0.658341	0.000000
445	0.386726	0.074704	2.027300	605	1.089100	0.593878	0.000000
450	0.370702	0.089456	1.994800	610	1.030480	0.527963	0.000000
455	0.342957	0.106256	1.900700	615	0.950740	0.461834	0.000000
460	0.302273	0.128201	1.745370	620	0.856297	0.398057	0.000000
465	0.254085	0.152761	1.554900	625	0.754930	0.339554	0.000000
470	0.195618	0.185190	1.317560	630	0.647467	0.283493	0.000000
475	0.132349	0.219940	1.030200	635	0.535110	0.228254	0.000000
480	0.080507	0.253589	0.772125	640	0.431567	0.179828	0.000000
485	0.041072	0.297665	0.570600	645	0.343690	0.140211	0.000000
490	0.016172	0.339133	0.415254	650	0.268329	0.107633	0.000000
495	0.005132	0.395379	0.302356	655	0.204300	0.081187	0.000000
500	0.003816	0.460777	0.218502	660	0.152568	0.060281	0.000000
505	0.015444	0.531360	0.159249	665	0.112210	0.044096	0.000000
510	0.037465	0.606741	0.112044	670	0.081261	0.031800	0.000000
515	0.071358	0.685660	0.082248	675	0.057930	0.022602	0.000000

Table 4.3 Continued.

Wave-length in nm	$\bar{x}_{10}(\lambda)$	$\bar{y}_{10}(\lambda)$	$\bar{z}_{10}(\lambda)$	Wave-length in nm	$\bar{x}_{10}(\lambda)$	$\bar{y}_{10}(\lambda)$	$\bar{z}_{10}(\lambda)$
680	0.040851	0.015905	0.000000	760	0.000126	0.000050	0.000000
685	0.028623	0.011130	0.000000	765	0.000090	0.000035	0.000000
690	0.019941	0.007749	0.000000	770	0.000065	0.000025	0.000000
695	0.013842	0.005375	0.000000	775	0.000046	0.000018	0.000000
700	0.009577	0.003718	0.000000	780	0.000033	0.000013	0.000000
705	0.006605	0.002564	0.000000	785	0.000024	0.000010	0.000000
710	0.004553	0.001768	0.000000	790	0.000018	0.000007	0.000000
715	0.003145	0.001222	0.000000	795	0.000013	0.000005	0.000000
720	0.002175	0.000846	0.000000	800	0.000009	0.000004	0.000000
725	0.001506	0.000586	0.000000	805	0.000007	0.000003	0.000000
730	0.001045	0.000407	0.000000	810	0.000005	0.000002	0.000000
735	0.000727	0.000284	0.000000	815	0.000004	0.000001	0.000000
740	0.000508	0.000199	0.000000	820	0.000003	0.000001	0.000000
745	0.000356	0.000139	0.000000	825	0.000002	0.000001	0.000000
750	0.000251	0.000098	0.000000	830	0.000002	0.000001	0.000000
755	0.000178	0.000070	0.000000				

4.3 Tristimulus values *X*, *Y*, *Z*

By analogy, with Eqs. (3.10), (3.11), and (3.12) it is easy to see that the tristimulus values for a nonmonochromatic light source with spectral radiance $P(\lambda)$ are given by

$$X = \int_0^\infty P(\lambda)\,\bar{x}(\lambda)\,\mathrm{d}\lambda\ , \qquad (4.14)$$

$$Y = \int_0^\infty P(\lambda)\,\bar{y}(\lambda)\,\mathrm{d}\lambda\ , \qquad (4.15)$$

and

$$Z = \int_0^\infty P(\lambda)\,\bar{z}(\lambda)\,\mathrm{d}\lambda\ . \qquad (4.16)$$

As described in Chapter 1, the maximum photopic relative luminous efficiency of the human eye is about 683 lumens per watt, at a wavelength of

555 nm. Thus, from Eq. (1.10), for a polychromatic light source the luminance $\overline{L}$ in lumens is given by

$$\overline{L} = 683 \int_0^\infty P(\lambda) V(\lambda) \, \mathrm{d}\lambda = 683 \, Y \, . \tag{4.17}$$

This means that as desired, the luminosity is given only by the tristimulus value Y. From Eq. (1.11), the luminous efficiency σ of a light source in lumens per watt is given by

$$\sigma = 683 \frac{Y}{\overline{P}} \, , \tag{4.18}$$

where $\overline{P}$ is the radiance.

4.4 Chromaticity coordinates x, y, z

As in the case of the r, g, b space, the chromaticity coordinates for spectrally pure colors are found by normalizing the color-matching functions for the wavelength, as

$$x(\lambda) = \frac{\overline{x}(\lambda)}{\overline{x}(\lambda) + \overline{y}(\lambda) + \overline{z}(\lambda)} \, , \tag{4.19}$$

$$y(\lambda) = \frac{\overline{y}(\lambda)}{\overline{x}(\lambda) + \overline{y}(\lambda) + \overline{z}(\lambda)} \, , \tag{4.20}$$

and

$$z(\lambda) = \frac{\overline{z}(\lambda)}{\overline{x}(\lambda) + \overline{y}(\lambda) + \overline{z}(\lambda)} \, . \tag{4.21}$$

For the case of a color with several wavelengths, the corresponding chromaticity coordinates are

$$x = \frac{X}{X + Y + Z} \, , \tag{4.22}$$

$$y = \frac{Y}{X + Y + Z} \, , \tag{4.23}$$

and

$$z = \frac{Z}{X + Y + Z} \, . \tag{4.24}$$

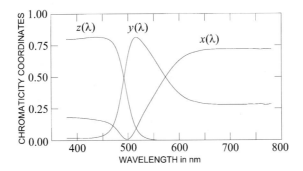

Figure 4.4 Chromaticity coordinates $x(\lambda)$, $y(\lambda)$ and $z(\lambda)$ for spectrally pure colors for a 2-deg field (CIE 1931).

These chromaticity coordinates, illustrated in Fig. 4.4, are nonlinearly independent from each other, since they are related by

$$x + y + z = 1 .\qquad\qquad (4.25)$$

See Table 4.4 for the numerical values of the chromaticity coordinates $x(\lambda)$, $y(\lambda)$ and $z(\lambda)$ for spectrally pure monochromatic colors, for a field of two degrees, given to four decimal places.

Table 4.4 Numerical values of the chromaticity coordinates $x(\lambda)$, $y(\lambda)$, and $z(\lambda)$ for spectrally pure monochromatic colors and a field of 2-deg (CIE, 1932).

Wave-length in nm	$x(\lambda)$	$y(\lambda)$	$z(\lambda)$	Wave-length in nm	$x(\lambda)$	$y(\lambda)$	$z(\lambda)$
380	0.1741	0.0050	0.8209	440	0.1644	0.0109	0.8247
385	0.1740	0.0050	0.8210	445	0.1611	0.0138	0.8251
390	0.1738	0.0049	0.8213	450	0.1566	0.0177	0.8257
395	0.1736	0.0049	0.8215	455	0.1510	0.0227	0.8263
400	0.1733	0.0048	0.8219	460	0.1440	0.0297	0.8263
405	0.1730	0.0048	0.8222	465	0.1355	0.0399	0.8246
410	0.1726	0.0048	0.8226	470	0.1241	0.0578	0.8181
415	0.1721	0.0048	0.8231	475	0.1096	0.0868	0.8036
420	0.1714	0.0051	0.8235	480	0.0913	0.1327	0.7760
425	0.1703	0.0058	0.8239	485	0.0687	0.2007	0.7306
430	0.1689	0.0069	0.8242	490	0.0454	0.2950	0.6596
435	0.1669	0.0086	0.8245	495	0.0235	0.4127	0.5638

Table 4.4 Continued.

Wave-length in nm	$x(\lambda)$	$y(\lambda)$	$z(\lambda)$	Wave-length in nm	$x(\lambda)$	$y(\lambda)$	$z(\lambda)$
500	0.0082	0.5384	0.4534	645	0.7230	0.2770	0.0000
505	0.0039	0.6548	0.3413	650	0.7260	0.2740	0.0000
510	0.0139	0.7502	0.2359	655	0.7283	0.2717	0.0000
515	0.0389	0.8120	0.1491	660	0.7300	0.2700	0.0000
520	0.0743	0.8338	0.0919	665	0.7311	0.2689	0.0000
525	0.1142	0.8262	0.0596	670	0.7320	0.2680	0.0000
530	0.1547	0.8059	0.0394	675	0.7327	0.2673	0.0000
535	0.1929	0.7816	0.0255	680	0.7334	0.2666	0.0000
540	0.2296	0.7543	0.0161	685	0.7340	0.2660	0.0000
545	0.2658	0.7243	0.0099	690	0.7344	0.2656	0.0000
550	0.3016	0.6923	0.0061	695	0.7346	0.2654	0.0000
555	0.3373	0.6589	0.0038	700	0.7347	0.2653	0.0000
560	0.3731	0.6245	0.0024	705	0.7347	0.2653	0.0000
565	0.4087	0.5796	0.0017	710	0.7347	0.2653	0.0000
570	0.4441	0.5547	0.0012	715	0.7347	0.2653	0.0000
575	0.4788	0.5202	0.0010	720	0.7347	0.2653	0.0000
580	0.5125	0.4866	0.0009	725	0.7347	0.2653	0.0000
585	0.5448	0.4544	0.0008	730	0.7347	0.2653	0.0000
590	0.5752	0.4242	0.0006	735	0.7347	0.2653	0.0000
595	0.6029	0.3965	0.0006	740	0.7347	0.2653	0.0000
600	0.6270	0.3725	0.0005	745	0.7347	0.2653	0.0000
605	0.6482	0.3514	0.0004	750	0.7347	0.2653	0.0000
610	0.6658	0.3340	0.0002	755	0.7347	0.2653	0.0000
615	0.6801	0.3197	0.0002	760	0.7347	0.2653	0.0000
620	0.6915	0.3083	0.0002	765	0.7347	0.2653	0.0000
625	0.7006	0.2993	0.0001	770	0.7347	0.2653	0.0000
630	0.7079	0.2920	0.0001	775	0.7347	0.2653	0.0000
635	0.7140	0.2859	0.0001	780	0.7347	0.2653	0.0000
640	0.7190	0.2809	0.0001				

The values of the chromaticity coordinates r, g, and b for each of the three stimuli X, Y, and Z, defined by the points (1, 0, 0), (0, 1, 0), and (0, 0, 1) in the x-y color space are obtained by normalizing the values in Table 4.1, as shown in Table 4.5.

A representation of *x* vs. *y* values is known as the CIE chromaticity diagram (Fig. 4.5) with all spectrally pure colors represented along the horseshoe-like curve. A straight line joining the extremes of this curve represents the purple colors, formed by a combination of red with blue in different proportions. The luminosity cannot be represented in this diagram, only the saturation and the hue of the color (Fig. 4.6). So, the point with coordinates $x = 0.33$ and $y = 0.33$ represents not only the white color, but also black and all gray colors. In the same manner, any other point can have any luminosity. A complete specification for any given color would be given by the chromaticity coordinates of *x* and *y* and the luminosity of *Y*.

The values of the chromaticity coordinates *r*, *g* and *b* for each of the three stimuli *X*, *Y* and *Z*, defined by the points (1, 0, 0), (0, 1, 0) and (0, 0, 1) in the *x-y* color space are obtained by normalizing the values in Table 4.1, as shown in Table 4.6.

Table 4.5 Chromaticity coordinates (on the inclined plane passing through the unit vectors) *r*, *g*, and *b* for each of the three stimuli *X*, *Y*, and *Z*, for a 2-deg field.

Point (x, y, z)	r	g	b
(1, 0, 0)	1.275	−0.278	0.003
(0, 1, 0)	−1.738	2.765	−0.028
(0, 0, 1)	−0.743	0.141	1.602

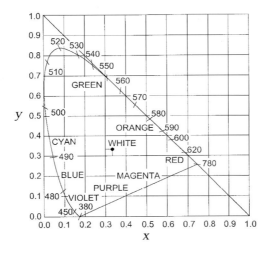

Figure 4.5 Chromaticity *x – y* diagram for a 10-deg (CIE 1964).

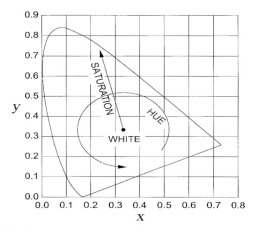

Figure 4.6 Hue and saturation variation in the chromaticity diagram.

Table 4.6 Numerical values of the chromaticity coordinates $x_{10}(\lambda)$, $y_{10}(\lambda)$, and $z_{10}(\lambda)$ for the spectrally pure monochromatic colors, for a field of 10 deg, given to four decimal places (CIE, 1964).

Wave-length in nm	$x_{10}(\lambda)$	$y_{10}(\lambda)$	$z_{10}(\lambda)$	Wave-length in nm	$x_{10}(\lambda)$	$y_{10}(\lambda)$	$z_{10}(\lambda)$
380	0.1813	0.0197	0.7990	470	0.1152	0.1090	0.7758
385	0.1809	0.0195	0.7995	475	0.0957	0.1591	0.7452
390	0.1803	0.0193	0.8003	480	0.0728	0.2292	0.6980
395	0.1795	0.0190	0.8015	485	0.0452	0.3273	0.6275
400	0.1784	0.0187	0.8029	490	0.0210	0.4401	0.5389
405	0.1771	0.0184	0.8045	495	0.0073	0.5625	0.4302
410	0.1755	0.0181	0.8064	500	0.0056	0.6745	0.3199
415	0.1732	0.0178	0.8090	505	0.0219	0.7526	0.2255
420	0.1706	0.0178	0.8115	510	0.0495	0.8023	0.1481
425	0.1679	0.0187	0.8134	515	0.0850	0.8169	0.0980
430	0.1650	0.0203	0.8147	520	0.1252	0.8102	0.0646
435	0.1622	0.0249	0.8153	525	0.1664	0.7922	0.0414
440	0.1590	0.0252	0.8152	530	0.2070	0.7963	0.0267
445	0.1554	0.0300	0.8146	535	0.2436	0.7399	0.0165
450	0.1510	0.0364	0.8126	540	0.2786	0.7113	0.0101
455	0.1459	0.0452	0.8088	545	0.3132	0.6813	0.0055
460	0.1389	0.0589	0.8021	550	0.3473	0.6501	0.0026
465	0.1295	0.0779	0.7926	555	0.3812	0.6182	0.0007

Table 4.6 Continued.

Wave-length in nm	$x_{10}(\lambda)$	$y_{10}(\lambda)$	$z_{10}(\lambda)$	Wave-length in nm	$x_{10}(\lambda)$	$y_{10}(\lambda)$	$z_{10}(\lambda)$
560	0.4142	0.5859	0.0000	675	0.7193	0.2806	0.0000
565	0.4469	0.5531	0.0000	680	0.7198	0.2802	0.0000
570	0.4790	0.5210	0.0000	685	0.7200	0.2800	0.0000
575	0.5096	0.4903	0.0000	690	0.7202	0.2798	0.0000
580	0.5386	0.4614	0.0000	695	0.7203	0.2797	0.0000
585	0.5654	0.4345	0.0000	700	0.7203	0.2796	0.0000
590	0.5900	0.4100	0.0000	705	0.7203	0.2797	0.0000
595	0.6116	0.3884	0.0000	710	0.7202	0.2798	0.0000
600	0.6306	0.3694	0.0000	715	0.7201	0.2799	0.0000
605	0.6471	0.3529	0.0000	720	0.7199	0.2801	0.0000
610	0.6612	0.3388	0.0000	725	0.7197	0.2803	0.0000
615	0.6730	0.3269	0.0000	730	0.7194	0.2805	0.0000
620	0.6827	0.3173	0.0000	735	0.7192	0.2808	0.0000
625	0.6897	0.3102	0.0000	740	0.7189	0.2811	0.0000
630	0.6955	0.3045	0.0000	745	0.7186	0.2814	0.0000
635	0.7010	0.2990	0.0000	750	0.7183	0.2817	0.0000
640	0.7059	0.2941	0.0000	755	0.7179	0.2820	0.0000
645	0.7102	0.2897	0.0000	760	0.7176	0.2824	0.0000
650	0.7137	0.2863	0.0000	765	0.7172	0.2828	0.0000
655	0.7156	0.2844	0.0000	770	0.7168	0.2831	0.0000
660	0.7158	0.2832	0.0000	775	0.7165	0.2835	0.0000
665	0.7179	0.2821	0.0000	780	0.7160	0.2839	0.0000
670	0.7187	0.2813	0.0000				

An approximate color representation of this chromaticity diagram can be seen in Fig. 4.7. This color representation cannot be made perfectly true in print or on a computer monitor for several reasons. One reason is that the primary colors used to produce this figure are colors located at the corners of the triangle in the CIE diagram. Thus, only colors inside this triangle can be accurately displayed. However, even if an infinite number of spectral colors could be used in the display, another practical problem arises—the luminance cannot be made constant over the whole diagram. This is because the alychne—that is the straight line representing the purple colors—has zero luminance, hence, all the points on

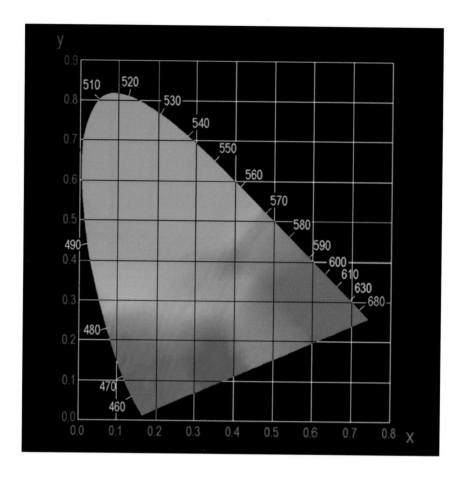

Figure 4.7 Color chromaticity $x - y$ diagram for a 2-deg field (CIE 1931).

the CIE chromaticity diagram would have zero luminosity. A diagram with any nonzero constant luminosity has to leave out the colors in the neighborhood of the alychne. A solution to the latter problem is to produce the color diagram with no constant luminance, which is frequently done.

In this the CIE diagram, we see Hering's concept of opponent colors (Krantz, 1975,) where red and green as well as blue and yellow are opposite colors, is correct since they are pairs on the opposite sides of the white point. In other words, if the proper proportions of red and green, yellow and blue are mixed, they will produce a white color.

Let us consider point A in the CIE diagram as shown in Fig. 4.8. Trace a line from the point W, representing white, to the curve representing the spectrally pure colors, and passing through the point A. The crossing point D between this line and this curve indicates the *dominant wavelength* of the color A, which is approximately related to the hue of this color. The *excitation purity p,* closely related to the *saturation* of color A, is given by

$$p = \frac{WA}{WD}. \qquad (4.26)$$

As we will see in Sec. 5.2, colors with a given dominant wavelength but a different excitation purity can have slightly different hues.

Now consider point B on the chromaticity diagram. The line from the white point W to point B does not pass through the spectrally pure colors curve; rather, it passes through the purples straight line. In this case, there is no dominant wavelength defined. Instead, we identify the *complementary wavelength* that is defined by the crossing point C of this line with the spectrally pure colors curve. Again, in this case the *excitation purity* of color B is given by

$$p = \frac{WB}{WC}. \qquad (4.27)$$

It is interesting to see in the CIE diagram (Fig. 4.9) the location of the chromaticity coordinates of blackbody radiators at different temperatures. As described in Chapter 2, if a colored body has the same chromaticity coordinates as a blackbody at temperature T the *color temperature* of this colored body or light source is T. Let us consider a colored body that does not have exactly same chromaticity coordinates as a blackbody radiator, but is close, as in the case of a D_{65} illuminant. In such a case, the temperature corresponding to the blackbody

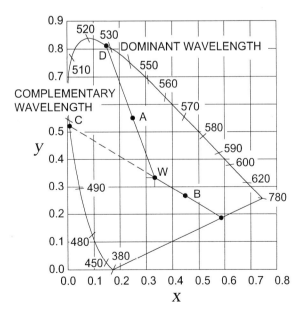

Figure 4.8 Dominant and complementary wavelengths in the chromaticity diagram.

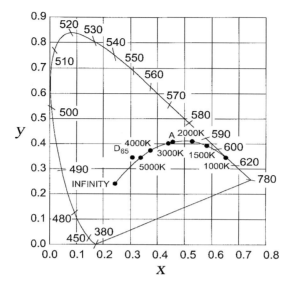

Figure 4.9 Colors of blackbody light sources for different temperatures.

with the closest chromaticity coordinates is said to be the *correlated color temperature*.

The tristimulus values X, Y, and Z for a spectrally pure (monochromatic) light source with wavelength λ and unit radiance $P(\lambda) = \overline{P}\,\delta(\lambda)$ can be written in terms of the luminous efficiency of the eye, $V(\lambda)$, and the chromaticity coordinates $x(\lambda)$, $y(\lambda)$, $z(\lambda)$ as

$$X = \overline{P}\,\frac{x(\lambda)}{y(\lambda)}\,V(\lambda) = \overline{P}\,\frac{\overline{x}(\lambda)}{\overline{y}(\lambda)}\,V(\lambda), \tag{4.28}$$

$$Y = \overline{P}\,V(\lambda), \tag{4.29}$$

and

$$Z = \overline{P}\,\frac{z(\lambda)}{y(\lambda)}\,V(\lambda) = \overline{P}\,\frac{\overline{z}(\lambda)}{\overline{y}(\lambda)}\,V(\lambda). \tag{4.30}$$

Thus, the tristimulus value Y for this monochromatic luminous object with unit radiance is equal to the normalized luminous efficiency of the eye, $V(\lambda)$, which, as $\overline{y}(\lambda)$, has a peak for a wavelength of about 550 nm. Obviously, the peak of y versus x is not the same. It is located at a wavelength close to 520 nm.

The CIE diagram was originally obtained in 1931 for a field diameter of 2 deg, but later in 1964 it was obtained for a field diameter of 10 deg, for the

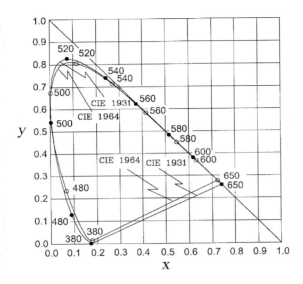

Figure 4.10 The two CIE chromaticity diagrams, for 2-deg and for 10-deg, shown for comparison.

reasons described in Chapter 3. These two diagrams are quite similar, as shown in Fig. 4.10.

Any color, with its hue, saturation, and luminance, can be specified by the tristimulus values X, Y, and Z, or by the chromaticity coordinates x, and y plus the tristimulus value Y. If x, y, and Y are known, the X and Z values can be obtained with

$$X = \frac{x}{y} Y ,$$ (4.31)

and

$$Z = \left(\frac{1}{y} - \frac{x}{y} - 1 \right) Y .$$ (4.32)

4.5 The color of a transparent or opaque body

When a transparent or opaque body is illuminated by a light source, its color has to be specified independently of the brightness of the light source illuminating it. However, the color of the light source—that is, the light's spectral radiance, or power spectrum—greatly influences the perceived color.

Printed or painted colors absorb part of the illuminating energy at some characteristic wavelengths and, thus, they reflect less than 100% of the illuminating light.

Consider an illuminating light source with a certain power spectrum represented by its spectral radiance $P(\lambda)$. Either the light passes through a colored transparent object, or it is reflected by a colored opaque body. The spectral transmittance $\tau(\lambda)$ of the filter or the spectral reflectance $\rho(\lambda)$ of the object are defined by the ratio of the exiting to the entering radiant fluxes, per unit wavelength interval, as described in Chapter 1. Then the observed spectral radiance of the illuminated object is directly proportional to the product of the spectral transmittance, or reflectance, and the illuminating spectral irradiance $W(\lambda)$. For example, neglecting the proportionality constant, in the case of an opaque object, the observed spectral radiance is

$$P(\lambda) = \rho(\lambda) W(\lambda). \tag{4.33}$$

The intrinsic color of an object can thus be defined as the perceived color when illuminated by the standard white light source. The natural theoretical choice is a white light source with a constant spectral irradiance of $W(\lambda) = 1$. However, this is not practical, because this light source does not exist in nature. A better choice for this reference light source is a standard illuminant. A perfectly white opaque object with $\rho(\lambda) = 1$ will reflect light with a power spectrum equal to that of the chosen illuminant. Thus, the white body has the maximum *luminous reflectance* that an opaque body may have, equal to 100. The minimum luminous reflectance is that of a blackbody, equal to zero. Thus, the tristimulus values defining the color of an opaque object are therefore expressed as

$$X = 100 \frac{\sum_{i=1}^{N} P_{st}(\lambda_i) \, \rho(\lambda_i) \, \overline{x}(\lambda_i)}{\sum_{i=1}^{N} P_{st}(\lambda_i) \, \overline{y}(\lambda_i)}, \tag{4.34}$$

$$Y = 100 \frac{\sum_{i=1}^{N} P_{st}(\lambda_i) \, \rho(\lambda) \, \overline{y}(\lambda_i)}{\sum_{i=1}^{N} P_{st}(\lambda_i) \, \overline{y}(\lambda_i)}, \tag{4.35}$$

and

$$Z = 100 \frac{\sum_{i=1}^{N} P_{st}(\lambda_i) \, \rho(\lambda) \, \overline{z}(\lambda_i)}{\sum_{i=1}^{N} P_{st}(\lambda_i) \, \overline{y}(\lambda_i)}, \tag{4.36}$$

where these values have been normalized so that the luminous reflectance of a perfectly white object is 100, $P_{st}(\lambda)$ is the spectral radiance or power spectrum of the standard illuminant being used, and $\rho(\lambda)$ is the spectral reflectance of the colored opaque body. Both of these spectra are in a scale from zero to 1. For the case of a colored filter or a transparent colored object, the spectral reflectance $\rho(\lambda)$ is replaced by the spectral transmittance $\tau(\lambda)$. It must be noted that the tristimulus Y value is equal to the luminous reflectance (or luminous transmittance) of an opaque (or transparent) colored body. The denominator in these expressions represents the luminance of the illuminating light beam.

The tristimulus values X_n, Y_n, and Z_n for a white opaque object with constant spectral reflectance [$\rho(\lambda) = 1$] (also called a perfect diffuser), when illuminated with a standard illuminant are

$$X_n = 100 \frac{\sum_{i=1}^{N} P_{st}(\lambda_i)\, \bar{x}(\lambda_i)}{\sum_{i=1}^{N} P_{st}(\lambda_i)\, \bar{y}(\lambda_i)}, \qquad (4.37)$$

$$Y_n = 100, \qquad (4.38)$$

and

$$Z_n = 100 \frac{\sum_{i=1}^{N} P_{st}(\lambda_i)\, \bar{z}(\lambda_i)}{\sum_{i=1}^{N} P_{st}(\lambda_i)\, \bar{y}(\lambda_i)}. \qquad (4.39)$$

The values of the denominators are listed in Table 4.7.

Table 4.7 Tristimulus values X_n, Y_n, Z_n for a white opaque object with a constant unit spectral reflectance. The last column lists the values of the denominator in Eqs. (4.37), (4.38), and (4.39).

Illum.	Observer	X_n	Y_n	Z_n	x_n	z_n	Denom.
A	2-deg	109.850	100.000	35.585	0.448	0.407	2157.94
	10-deg	111.144	100.000	35.201	0.451	0.406	2275.83
D_{65}	2-deg	95.053	100.000	108.900	0.313	0.329	2113.41
	10-deg	94.812	100.000	107.327	0.314	0.331	2324.08

If no incident energy is absorbed in any opaque or transparent colored body, the body is white. However, the appearance of color requires the absorption of part of the incident light energy. The spectral reflectance or the spectral transmittance defines the dominant wavelength, the purity, and the luminous reflectance or transmittance of the body. If we select particular values for any two of these three quantities, there is an infinite number of different spectral reflectances or spectral transmittances that give us the two desired values. For example, given the luminous reflectance or the luminous transmittance value and the dominant wavelength, there is an infinite number of spectral reflectance or spectral transmittance curves with an infinite number of purity values.

To better understand these important concepts, let us assume that we illuminate a diffuse colored reflecting surface with a standard illuminant, for example, D_{65}. If the surface is reflecting [$\rho(\lambda) = 1$] perfectly in a certain narrow wavelength interval, the reflected beam has the power spectrum illustrated in Fig. 4.11. Let us further assume that the reflected light has a dominant wavelength, λ_0.

Another power spectrum, represented by the dotted line in the same figure, has the same luminance and is the same dominant wavelength. As easily observed and proven by McAdam (1935a and 1935b), the power spectrum with the straight boundaries has the highest purity (lowest saturation). Figure 4.12 shows the spectra of four light sources with the same dominant wavelength. These light sources have the maximum possible purity with increasing luminance levels.

A consequence of the former analysis is that given a constant fixed luminance, for any dominant wavelength there is a maximum possible purity value. When the maximum luminous reflectance value is equal to 100, only the white color is possible.

Following a slightly different line of thought, the dotted power spectrum in Fig. 4.11 can be narrowed, preserving the same dominant wavelength so the two spectra have the same purity (instead of the same luminance). Thus, they will have the same position on the chromaticity diagram. The color with the power spectrum having straight boundaries has the maximum possible luminance.

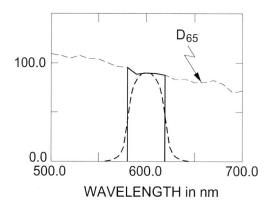

Figure 4.11 Two spectral curves with the same dominant wavelength and luminance.

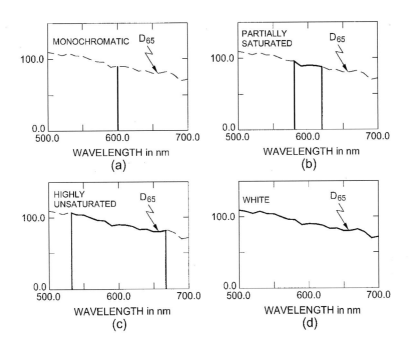

Figure 4.12 Four spectral curves. (a) A spectrally pure color, (b) a partially saturated color with straight boundaries, (c) a highly unsaturated color with straight boundaries and (d) a white color.

The maximum attainable purity for a given dominant wavelength and luminance depends on the type of illuminant (Fig. 4.13) for an incandescent tungsten lamp with CIE illuminant A (2854 K) and for artificial daylight with CIE illuminant C (Fig. 4.14). The important conclusion is that the gamut of all physically attainable colors is gradually reduced as the reflectance (luminosity) of the color becomes larger. An approximate representation of this possible gamut of color for different types of illuminance with daylight is illustrated in Fig 4.15. The boundary of this gamut of colors for each reflectance value is frequently called the MacAdam limit.

If we represent the luminance along the z-axis, perpendicular to both the x- and y-axes, the closed curves representing the MacAdam limits for luminance (Fig. 4.13) will be at different heights z, forming a space volume. This is the CIE color-space solid with the CIE illuminant D_{65} (Fig. 4.16).

MacAdam (1950) proved the curves on the CIE chromaticity diagram with the maximum possible luminous efficiency in lumens per watt are as shown in Fig. 4.17. As expected, we see that the maximum possible luminous efficiency in the whole diagram corresponds to a monochromatic spectral color with a wavelength of 555 nm and 683 lumens per watt.

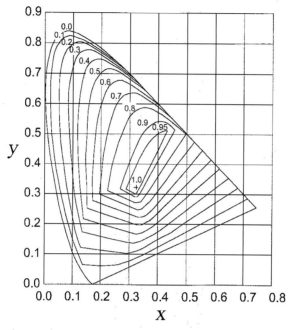

Figure 4.13 The locus of points with maximum possible purity of reflected (or transmitted) light, or MacAdam limits, in nonfluorescent objects in incandescent tungsten lamp with color temperature 2854 K (illuminant A).

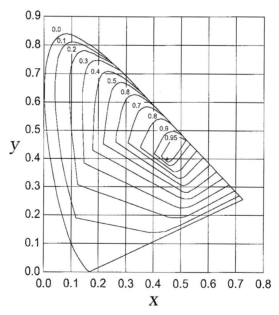

Figure 4.14 The locus of points with maximum possible purity of reflected (or transmitted) light, or MacAdam limits, in nonfluorescent objects in artificial daylight (illuminant D_{65}).

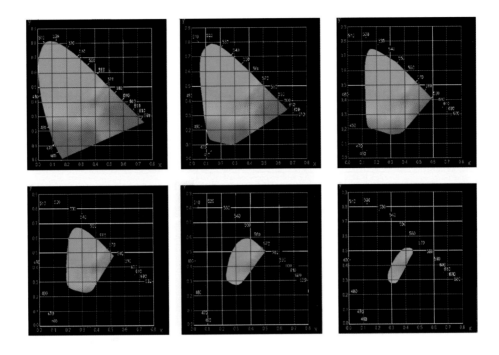

Figure 4.15 The gamut of possible colors for different values of the luminance with artificial daylight illumination.

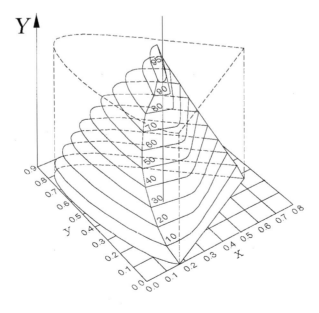

Figure 4.16 CIE (*x, y, z*) color solid.

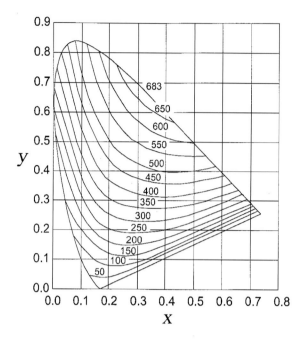

Figure 4.17 The locus of points with maximum attainable luminous efficiency (lumens per watt) for colors in the CIE chromaticity diagram.

References

CIE, Commission Internationale de l'Éclairage Proceedings, 1931, Cambridge, Cambridge University Press (1932).

CIE Vienna Session, (Committee Report E–1.4.1), *Bureau Central de la CIE*, 1963, Vol. B, pp. 209–220 Paris (1964).

Ives H. E., "The Transformation of Color-Mixture Equations from One System to Another," *J. Franklin Inst.*, pp. 180, 673 (1915).

Ives H. E., "The Transformation of Color-Mixture Equations from One System to Another II. Graphical Aids," *J. Franklin Inst.*, 195, pp. 23 (1923).

Krantz D. H., "Color Measurement and Color Theory: II Opponent-Colors Theory," *J. of Mathematical Psychology,* 12, pp. 304–327 (1975).

MacAdam D. L., "The Theory of the Maximum Visual Efficiency of Colored Materials," *J. Opt. Soc. Am.*, 25, pp. 249–252 (1935a).

MacAdam D. L., "Maximum Visual Efficiency of Colored Materials," *J. Opt. Soc. Am.*, 25, pp. 261–367 (1935b).

MacAdam D. L., "Maximum Attainable Luminous Efficiency of Various Chromaticities," *J. Opt. Soc. Am.*, 40, pp. 120–120 (1950).

Chapter 5
Uniform Color Systems

5.1 Introduction

A small displacement in the CIE color space coordinates X, Y, Z will not produce the same change in the perceived color at any point or any direction of change. Similarly, any displacement in the CIE chromaticity diagram will not produce a constant change in hue and saturation. The minimum displacement to be able to detect a color change in the CIE diagram is represented by the MacAdam (1942, 1943) ellipses shown in Fig. 5.1, where they have been drawn ten times larger for clarity. Very small changes can be detected near the blue end of the diagram. On the other hand, purity (saturation) changes in the green region are difficult to detect.

Ellipsoids in a three-dimensional space that include small differences in lightness (luminance) have also been obtained by Brown and MacAdam (1949) and by Brown (1957). However, these ellipsoids are difficult to use, and attempts made to develop algebraic expressions for them have been unsuccessful.

Ideally, the CIE color space is modified by means of a linear transformation obtaining a representation on which the minimum perceived color changes in a transparent colored body, or in an opaque colored body, are almost equal at any point and in any direction, which transforms the ellipses into circles with a constant diameter. However, Silverstein (1943) has shown that this transformation is impossible.

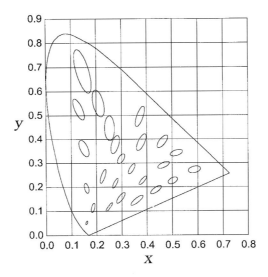

Figure 5.1 Color discrimination with McAdam ellipses, and equally noticeable color differences for 25 points. The ellipses are three times larger.

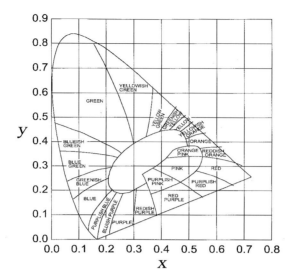

Figure 5.2 The names for some colors in the CIE chromaticity diagram. (K. L. Kelly, 1943).

Several color systems have been designed to obtain an approximately uniform color space. MacAdam (1971) proposed one system that nearly transformed the ellipses into circles. However, since the transformation is not linear, graphic rules for color addition do not work on this diagram. One other disadvantage is that there is no definite location for the white point. Another accepted system is the 1960 CIE chromaticity diagram in which the ellipses transform into a system with a smaller range of sizes, as we will see later in this chapter.

5.2 Hue and chroma in the chromaticity diagram

The measurements of hue, brightness, or saturation, as opposed to tristimulus values, are more in the realm of psychology than in the field of physics. Direct measurements are difficult to make; however, indirect measurements can be made, for example, by counting only perceptible intervals, as pointed out by Richardson (1932), but this is not a simple problem (Judd, 1962). The names of different colors Kelly (1943) indicated in a CIE diagram (Fig. 5.2) are all defined by hue and chroma.

We have seen in Sec. 4.4 that a straight line in the CIE diagram going from the white point to a point for a spectrally pure color is the locus of colors with the same dominant wavelength. However, the locus of points with the same hue is not a straight line since colors with the same dominant wavelength but a different chroma can have slightly different hues. According to Schrödinger (1920) the shortest path to neutral (white or gray) from any highly saturated color is that

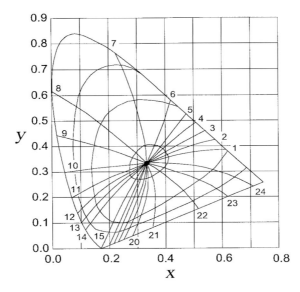

Figure 5.3 The locus of constant hue and constant chroma in the CIE chromaticity diagram.

which passes through colors with the same hue. Let us imagine the CIE diagram completely covered by the MacAdam ellipses. The path length between any two points could be defined as the number of ellipses being crossed from one point to the other. Thus, the shortest path between two points is that which crosses the minimum number of ellipses. Many efforts had been made to obtain the loci of a constant hue in the CIE diagram, as described by Judd (1972). An example is the constant hue curves derived by Muth and Persels (1971) and shown in Fig. 5.3. The constant chroma curves (Newhall, 1943) for a given value of the luminosity are closed curves around the neutral color (gray), also shown in Fig. 5.3.

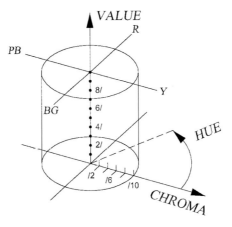

Figure 5.4 The Munsell color space.

5.3 The Munsell system

Around 1900, many years before the first CIE convention, Albert H. Munsell, an artist, empirically prepared a set of color charts with an almost uniform color representation. In the Munsell color space, the colors are represented in a cylinder with zero-saturation colors (black, gray, and white) along the axis. The coordinate's configuration in this space is illustrated in Fig. 5.4. The lowest extreme of the cylinder axis corresponds to black, while the highest extreme corresponds to white. The position along this axis, with ten steps from zero to nine, is called the *value*, representing the perceived lightness, which is nonlinear with the luminance Y. To take into account this nonlinearity, the value was originally taken as the square root of the luminance (Fig. 5.5), although it was later redefined to improve it.

The *chroma* represents the saturation of the color. It increases in a perpendicular direction to the axis, toward the edge of the cylinder, with values from zero to eight, and with monochromatic and purple colors around the periphery.

The *hue* of the color is represented by the angle. The Munsell circle is divided into the following 10 angular sectors with an angle of 36 deg: yellow (Y), yellow-red (YR), red (R), red-purple (RP), purple (P), purple-blue (PB), blue (B), blue-green (BG), green (G), and green-yellow (GY). Each of these sectors is divided into 10 sub-sectors with an angle of 3.6 deg. Figure 5.6 shows a Munsell circle inside the CIE diagram. In this system, the different colors are specified by *Hue Value/Chroma,* as in the following example: 4 YR 7/3, which means a yellow-red color in subsection 4 (hue = 4 YR) with lightness (value) = 7 and chroma = 3. Figure 5.7 shows a circle of colors with the same Munsell value.

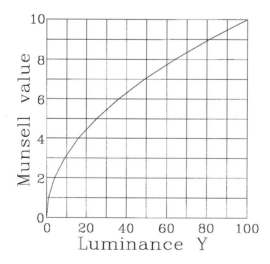

Figure 5.5 The magnitude of the Munsell value is equal to the square root of the luminance.

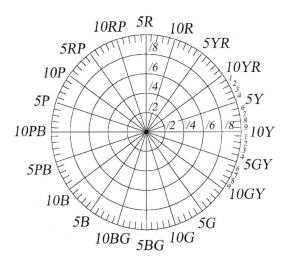

Figure 5.6 Organization of the colors in a Munsell circle with a constant value.

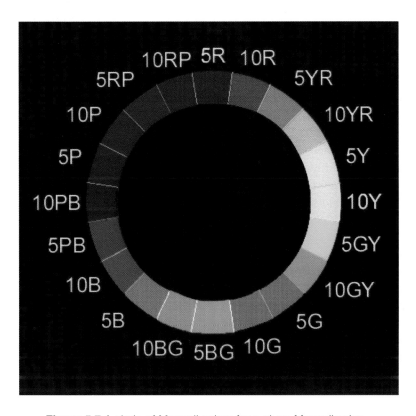

Figure 5.7 A circle of Munsell colors for a given Munsell value.

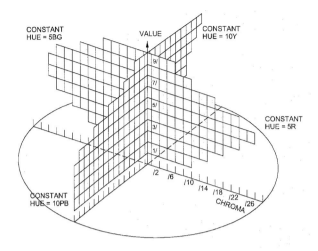

Figure 5.8 Four constant-hue planes in the Munsell color space.

In this system there are many planes with colors—one for each hue. A three-dimensional representation of all colors in the Munsell color space is formed by a series of radial planes with constant hue, as illustrated in Fig. 5.8. Thus, on each radial plane all colors have the same hue, but with the chroma increasing outward from the central axis, and the value increasing with height. It is interesting to note that not all planes have the same shape. They bulge outward for blue and purple colors at low values, and for yellow colors at high values. Only black is considered for the lowest value, while only white is represented for the highest value. We will see later in this chapter that these characteristics are also present in other uniform color spaces. Figure 5.9 is a close representation of the colors for four Munsell planes with different hues.

The original Munsell System was later modified to correct some obvious errors in the location of some colors. The new color designations and coordinates are known as *Munsell Renotations,* and the system is called the *Munsell Renotation System.*

The Munsell color system is almost perfectly uniform, where each color is separated from its closest neighbor by equal perceptual distances (Fig. 5.10) in comparison to the location of the same colors in the CIE *x-y* diagram. We can see that these curves closely resemble the constant chroma curves in Fig. 5.3.

An important practical disadvantage with the Munsell color system is that colors are defined only for a two-degrees observer and a C illuminant. Another problem with this system is that no analytical expressions to convert the CIE system to the Munsell system, or vice versa, exist. However, look-up table programs to perform these conversions have been proposed (Newhall, 1943, and Rheinboldt and Menard, 1960). Many attempts had been made to analytically define a color system that closely resembles the Munsell System, but without success. Some of these systems will be described in the following sections.

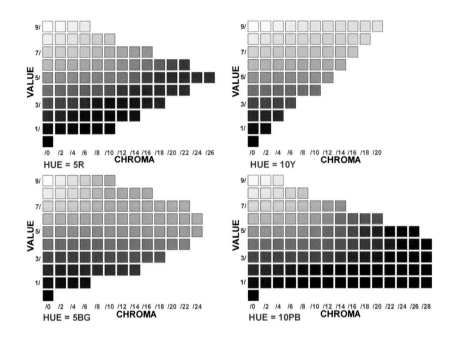

Figure 5.9 Approximate representation of the Munsell colors for four different hues.

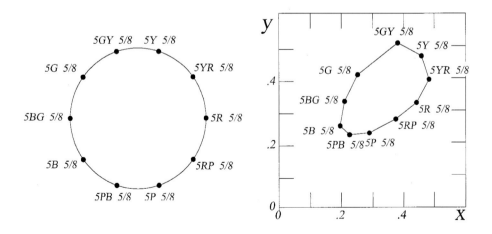

Figure 5.10 The relative location in a circle of some Munsell perceptually equally spaced colors, compared with their separation in a CIE *x y* diagram.

5.4 The 1960 CIE *L u v* color space

An almost uniform chromaticity diagram with coordinates $L\ u\ v$ proposed by the CIE convention in 1960, is based on the work by several researchers (MacAdam, 1937). This diagram was the result of an extensive search for a uniform color space by the Committee on Uniform Color Scales of the Optical Society of America, established in 1947. The committee's history of activities is related by Nickerson (1977). This space is defined by

$$u = \frac{4\,X}{X + 15\,Y + 3\,Z} = \frac{4\,x}{-2\,x + 12\,y + 3}, \qquad (5.1)$$

and

$$v = \frac{6\,Y}{X + 15\,Y + 3\,Z} = \frac{6\,x}{-2\,x + 12\,y + 3}, \qquad (5.2)$$

with its inverse transformation

$$x = \frac{6\,u}{6\,u - 16\,v + 12} \quad ; \quad y = \frac{4\,v}{6\,u - 16\,v + 12}. \qquad (5.3)$$

In the diagram shown in Fig. 5.11, the MacAdam ellipses are more uniform in size, and their eccentricities are smaller. A color representation of this diagram is shown in Fig. 5.12.

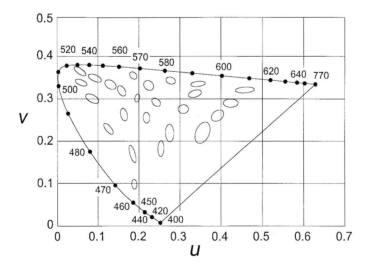

Figure 5.11 The *L u v* chromaticity diagram (CIE, 1960). MacAdam ellipses are ten-times larger.

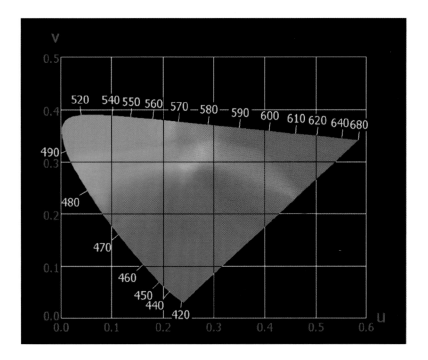

Figure 5.12 A color *L u v* chromaticity diagram (CIE, 1960).

Since this is a linear projective transformation, a great advantage is that a straight line in the *x, y* chromaticity diagram converts into another straight line in the *u-v* diagram. This property is important because it preserves the usual graphic rules for the addition of colors, as will be described in detail in Chapter 6.

In 1976, the CIE made a slight improvement to this diagram by defining a new chromaticity diagram (Fig. 5.13) with coordinates *u′ v′* defined by

$$u' = u ,\tag{5.4}$$

and

$$v' = 1.5\, v ,\tag{5.5}$$

thus obtaining

$$u' = \frac{4\,X}{X + 15\,Y + 3\,Z} = \frac{4\,x}{-2\,x + 12\,y + 3} ,\tag{5.6}$$

and

$$v' = \frac{9\,Y}{X + 15\,Y + 3\,Z} = \frac{9\,x}{-2\,x + 12\,y + 3} .\tag{5.7}$$

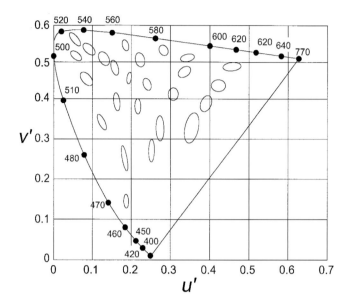

Figure 5.13 The $L'\,u'\,v'$ chromaticity diagram (CIE, 1960). MacAdam ellipses are ten-times larger.

5.5 The 1976 CIE $L^*\,u^*\,v^*$ color space

In 1976, the CIE Convention recommended the $L^*\,u^*\,v^*$ color space, abbreviated as CIELUV, for use in the television and video display industries. This space is a modification of the u', v' system, defined by

$$L^* = 116\, f\!\left(\frac{Y}{Y_n}\right) - 16 ,\tag{5.8}$$

$$u^* = 13L^* \left[u' - u_n\right]\tag{5.9}$$

and

$$v^* = 13L^* \left[v' - v_n\right]\tag{5.10}$$

This color space is not used alone but almost always as an intermediate step leading to the use of the CIE $L^*\,u^*\,v^*$ color space.

As pointed out before, the perceived lightness L is not linear with the luminance Y. Here, it is defined by the nonlinear cubic root function $f(s)$ defined as $f(s) = 7.787s + 16/116$ for values of $s \le 0.008856$, and by $f(s) = s^{1/3}$ for values of $s > 0.008856$. This equation improves the original square root function. There is no discontinuity in either the value of the function or their slope at the point where both definitions join, as shown in Fig. 5.14. The values of u_n and v_n are the coordinates for a nominal white color, which can be calculated using the tristimulus values X_n, Y_n, and Z_n corresponding to the perfect diffuser when illuminated with a standard illuminant such as D_{65}. Therefore, the standard illuminant location in the u^*, v^* diagram is always the origin.

We see that the expression for the coordinates u^* and v^* are multiplied by the value of the luminance L^*. So, in a $u^* v^*$ diagram, a color with a certain hue and chroma is not uniquely represented with the same values of $u^* v^*$, and for all possible values of the luminance. The only exceptions are for the neutral colors (white, gray, and black), which are at $u^* = v^* = 0$, since those coordinate values depend on the value of L^*. However, the property that a straight line in the x, y diagram transforms into a straight line in the $u^* v^*$ diagram is valid if L^* is constant. A sketch of the CIE $L^* u^* v^*$ color solid is illustrated in Fig. 5.15. The locus of all monochromatic colors for all possible luminance values is in the shape of a cone with a vertex at the origin, since the coordinates u^*, v^* are multiplied by the luminance. The reason for this conical shape is that as the luminance decreases, the color differences are more difficult to perceive—that is, the MacAdam ellipses grow in size, thus all colors converge to the black point when the luminance becomes zero.

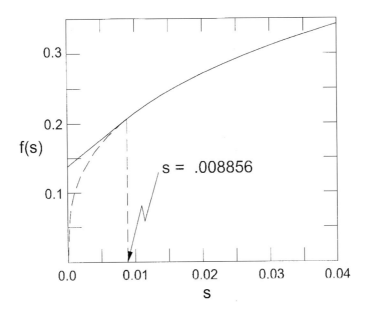

Figure 5.14 Function $f(s)$ for CIE $L' u' v'$ and CIE $L^* a^* b^*$ color space.

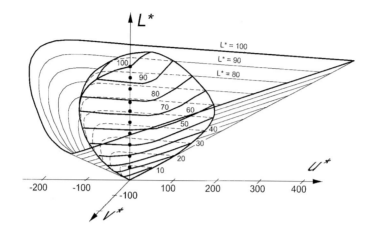

Figure 5.15 The $L^*u^*v^*$ color solid (CIE, 1976).

If the transformation equations are applied to the CIE horseshoe-shaped locus of the monochromatic colors for many values of the luminance, a conical surface with a vertex at the zero-luminance black color is obtained. However, as described in Sec. 4.5, as the luminance increases, the maximum possible purity for a given dominant wavelength decreases, producing the MacAdam limits. These limits shrink the gamut of possible colors for a given luminance, becoming a point for the maximum possible value of the luminance, representing the white color. Then, as expected, for the minimum and maximum values of the luminosity—0 and 100, respectively—only the neutral colors (black and white) are possible.

The CIELUV color difference equation is

$$\Delta E_{uv}^* = \left[\ (\Delta L^*)^2 + (\Delta u^*)^2 + (\Delta v^*)^2 \ \right]^{1/2}, \qquad (5.11)$$

where

$$\Delta L^* = L^* - L_{ref}^*$$

$$\Delta u^* = u^* - u_{ref}^* \qquad (5.12)$$

$$\Delta v^* = v^* - v_{ref}^*$$

where the subscript *ref* stands for the reference or target value. A positive value of ΔL^* means that the measured color is lighter than the reference value; otherwise it is negative. A positive value of Δu^* means than the sample is too red; a negative value means it is too green. A positive value of Δv^* means than the sample is too yellow; a negative value means it is too blue.

In some instances, instead of specifying the color by L^* u^* and v^*, the quantities L^*, C^*, and h^* are used, where

$$C^* = \left[u^{*2} + v^{*2} \right]^{1/2}, \tag{5.13}$$

is the saturation, or chroma, and

$$h^* = \arctan \left[\frac{v^*}{u^*} \right]^{1/2}, \tag{5.14}$$

is the hue angle with a zero value along the u^* axis.

5.6 The Hunter *L a b* color space

For many years, R. S. Hunter tried to design a good uniform color system by using the Munsell colors as a reference. His most successful color space was the *L a b* (Hunter and Harols, 1987). He represented the lightness L, as in the Munsell system, by the square root of the luminance Y along the z-axis in a Cartesian system of coordinates. The maximum value of the lightness, equal to 100, is for a perfect white while the minimum value, equal to zero, is for black.

Hunter based his system on the fact discovered by Herring and later confirmed by the CIE diagram, that red and green are opposite colors, as are blue and yellow. The a value represents the redness on the positive side and the greenness on the negative side. In the same manner, the b value represents the yellowness on the positive side and the blueness on the negative side.

By subtracting the value of the tristimulus X from the value of Y and also the value of Y from the value of Z, an opponent color type system was obtained. The equations used to transform the CIE x, y system to the Hunter L a b system are

$$L^* = 100 \left(\frac{Y}{Y_n} \right)^{1/2}, \tag{5.15}$$

$$a = 1.785\, X_n \frac{\left[\left(\dfrac{X}{X_n} \right) - \left(\dfrac{Y}{Y_n} \right) \right]}{\left(\dfrac{Y}{Y_n} \right)^{1/2}}, \tag{5.16}$$

and

$$b = 0.5929\, Z_n \frac{\left[\left(\dfrac{Y}{Y_n}\right) - \left(\dfrac{Z}{Z_n}\right)\right]}{\left(\dfrac{Y}{Y_n}\right)^{1/2}}, \tag{5.17}$$

where the opposite colors are on the opposite sides of a line passing through the perfect white with tristimulus values X_n, Y_n, Z_n. This reference white can be used for the 2-deg or the 10-deg observer, and for any desired standard illuminant as well. The constants in front of the expression for a and b had been chosen so that the color system is as uniform as possible.

It can easily be shown that there is a line in the CIE x-y diagram that transforms into the red axis. This line can be found by setting $b = 0$ in the transformation equations. It passes through the reference white point, as described by the expression

$$x = 1 - \left(\frac{1 - x_n}{y_n}\right) y . \tag{5.18}$$

In a similar manner, by setting $a = 0$, the line on the CIE x-y diagram corresponding to the b axis is a line passing through the origin and the point for the reference white illuminant, as given by

$$x = \left(\frac{x_n}{y_n}\right) y . \tag{5.19}$$

As described above, the positive part of the a-axis is for the amount of a red-purple color and the negative part of the a-axis is for the amount of a green-cyan color. The positive part of the b axis is for the amount of yellow and the negative part of the b axis is for the amount of blue. These lines are illustrated in a CIE x-y diagram in Fig. 5.16.

A similar color space with opponent colors was designed by Adams and later modified by Nickerson. During the 1973 CIE meeting, David MacAdam proposed a modification to the existing opponent-color systems in an attempt to improve their deficiencies. At that time, the CIE L^* a^* b^* color system, described in next section, was proposed. However, it was difficult to decide between the L^* a^* b^* system and the previously described L^* u^* v^* system. Thus, after an extensive study both systems were accepted in 1976.

5.7 The 1976 CIE *L* a* b** color space

In 1976, the CIE Convention recommended the CIE L^* a^* b^*, or CIELAB, color space, mainly for use in the plastic, textile, and paint industries. As in the

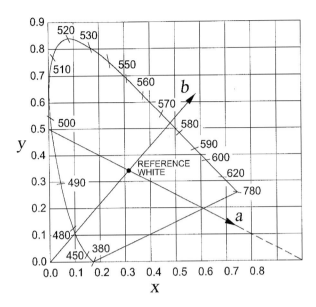

Figure 5.16 The *a*- and *b*-axes shown in the CIE-1964 chromaticity diagram (CIE, 1976).

Hunter space, the luminance is represented along the *z* axis in a Cartesian system of coordinates, with values from zero for black to 100 for a perfectly white body [constant reflectance $R(\lambda) = 1$]. The positive *a** axis represents the amount of a purplish red, while the negative *a** axis represents the amount of green. The positive *b** axis represents the amount of yellow, and the negative *b** axis represents the amount of blue. The maximum possible magnitude of the values on these axes is a function of the luminance in the range of -200 to 200.

The transformation equations to pass from the CIE *x, y, z* system to the CIE *L* a* b** system are

$$L^* = 116 f\left(\frac{Y}{Y_n}\right) - 16, \tag{5.20}$$

$$a^* = 500\left[f\left(\frac{X}{X_n}\right) - f\left(\frac{Y}{Y_n}\right) \right], \tag{5.21}$$

and

$$b^* = 200\left[f\left(\frac{Y}{Y_n}\right) - f\left(\frac{Z}{Z_n}\right) \right], \tag{5.22}$$

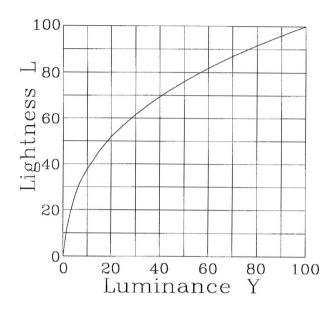

Figure 5.17 The plot of the lightness in the CIELAB system *vs*. the luminance.

where as in the $L\,a\,b$ and the $L^*\,u^*\,v^*$ systems, the lightness L^* is not linear with the luminance Y, as shown in Fig. 5.17. The nonfunction $f(s)$ is defined by $f(s) = 7.787s+16/116$ for values of $s \le 0.008856$ and by $f(s) = s^{1/3}$ for values of $s > 0.008856$. Also, as before, the tristimulus values X_n, Y_n, and Z_n correspond to the perfect diffuser when illuminated with the selected standard illuminant and average observer (see Sec. 4.5). In the $a^*\,b^*$ diagram, as in the preceding systems, the standard illuminant is located at the origin.

At the point $a^*=b^*=0$, which is the L^* axis, the neutral color has a well-defined location, but any other color does not have a unique location as $a^*\,b^*$ is independent of the value of L^*. The lines in the x-y diagram that transform into the a^* and b^* axes are the same as in the Hunter system, as illustrated in Fig. 5.16.

When the transformation equations are applied to the CIE locus of the monochromatic colors for many values of the luminance, the curves in Fig. 5.18 are obtained. We can observe that the line where the purple colors are located is transformed into a curve in the $a^*\,b^*$ plane. When these curves are plotted in a three-dimensional space with the lightness at the third axis, a conic surface with its vertex at the black point is obtained. However, as described in Sec. 4.5, when the luminance increases, the gamut of color for any given luminance decreases for high values of the luminance, producing the MacAdam limits. This gamut of possible colors for a given luminance becomes a point for the maximum value of the luminance, representing white. Thus, for the minimum and maximum values

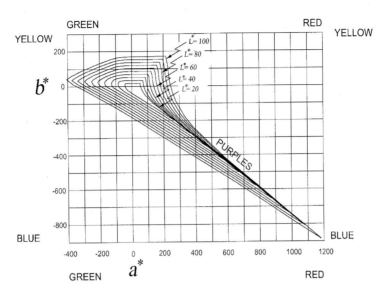

Figure 5.18 The locus of spectrally pure and purple colors for different values of the lightness in the *a* b** plane.

of the lightness 0 and 100, respectively, only the neutral colors (black and white) are possible.

The size and shape of the regions representing the gamut of colors for different values of the luminance have an irregular shape and are plotted in Fig. 5.19. The maximum area of this region is close to a luminance equal to about 50. As in the CIE diagram, this zone of real colors is not a circle (see Figs. 4.15 and and 4.16), but has an irregular shape. In a rough approximation, the circular representation of the colors in this system is seen in Fig. 5.20

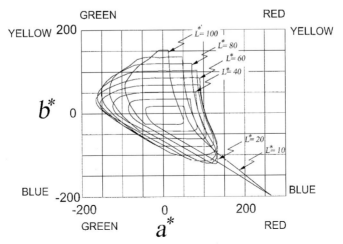

Figure 5.19 The gamut of all possible colors for different values of the luminance in the *a* b** plane.

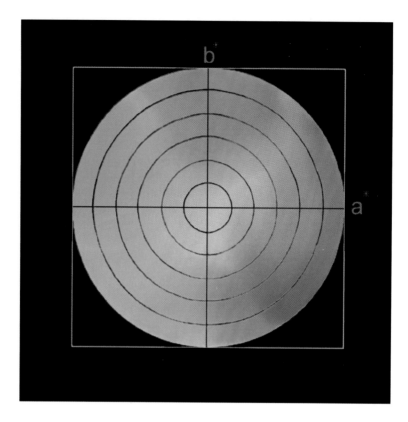

Figure 5.20 A color diagram representing in the approximate distribution of colors in the *a* b** plane.

We have seen that in this color system a line in the *x, y* diagram does not transform into a straight line, but into a curved line. Hence, the usual graphic rules for the addition of colors are not preserved. A sketch of the CIE *L* a* b** color solid can be found in Fig. 5.21. The locus of all monochromatic colors for all possible luminance values has an approximately conic shape with the smallest cross section at the origin. We can observe that for constant values of the luminance the locus of the purple colors is not a straight line as in the CIE *L* u* v** system. In the CIE *L* u* v** color system, the coordinates *a* b** are linearly dependent on the luminance, producing a conically shaped color solid in the vicinity of the black point—that is—near zero luminance. Because of the reasons described in Sec. 5.4, for large values of the luminance, all possible colors are located in a small area around the gray point, as defined by the MacAdam limits, and finally become a single point at the white color. Therefore, just as the CIE-*L* u* v** color solid contracts, the CIE *L* a* b** color solid also shrinks to a small spot for large and small values of the luminance.

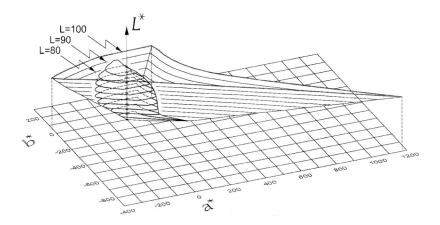

Figure 5.21 The L^* a^* b^* color solid (CIE 1976). For the sake of clarity the L^* scale has been amplified by a factor of ten with respect to the a^* and b^* axes.

Instead of specifying the color by L^* a^* and b^*, the quantities L^* C^* and h^* in polar coordinates can be used in what is known as the CIELCH system, where

$$C^*_{ab} = \left[a^{*2} + b^{*2} \right]^{1/2} \tag{5.23}$$

is the saturation, or chroma, and

$$h^*_{ab} = \arctan \left[\frac{b^*}{a^*} \right]^{1/2} \tag{5.24}$$

is the angle of the hue with a zero value along the a^* axis.

An evaluation of the uniformity of this system is shown in Fig. 5.22 where the locations of some perceived equally spaced Munsell colors are represented in the CIELAB color a^* b^* plane. As pointed out before, in a perfectly uniform color system, this diagram would be a circle. As a consequence, the tolerance volume is not a sphere but an ellipsoid, with different dimensions for hue, chroma, and luminance. Another consequence of the lack of uniformity in this system is that the tolerance ellipsoids do not have a constant size, as will be described in the next section. In this system, an average observer is most sensitive to hue differences, less sensitive to chroma differences, and least sensitive to luminance differences.

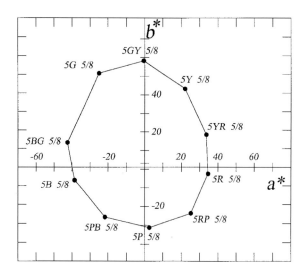

Figure 5.22 The relative location of some Munsell perceptually equally spaced colors in the CIELAB *a* b** diagram.

5.8 Color-difference equation in the CIE *L* a* b** color space

The CIELAB color-difference equation is the distance in the CIELAB diagram between the reference color and the measured color, given by

$$\Delta E_{ab}^* = \left[\ (\Delta L^*)^2 + (\Delta a^*)^2 + (\Delta b^*)^2\ \right]^{1/2}, \qquad (5.25)$$

where

$$\Delta L^* = L^* - L_{ref}^*,$$

$$\Delta a^* = a^* - a_{ref}^*, \qquad (5.26)$$

$$\Delta b^* = b^* - b_{ref}^*,$$

with the subscript *ref* standing for the reference or target value. A positive value of ΔL^* means that the measured color is lighter than the reference, and a negative value means it is darker. A positive value of Δa^* means than the sample is too red, or it is too green if Δa^* is negative. A positive value of Δb^* means than the sample is too yellow, or it is too blue if Δb^* is negative.

In the CIELCH system the chroma difference may be written as

$$\Delta C_{ab}^* = C_{ab}^* - C_{ab\,ref}^*, \qquad (5.27)$$

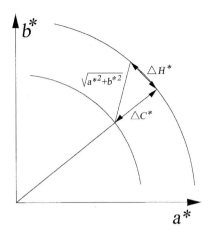

Figure 5.23 The distance between the measured point and the reference point in the $L^* a^* b^*$ diagram.

where a positive value indicates a higher chroma than the reference, and a negative value indicates a lower chroma. The hue difference is not calculated by the angle difference. It is given by the part that is left after taking lightness and chroma differences into account, as given by

$$\Delta H^*_{ab} = \left[(\Delta E^*_{ab})^2 - (\Delta L^*)^2 - (\Delta C^*_{ab})^2 \right]^{1/2}, \qquad (5.28)$$

which can also be written as

$$\Delta H^*_{ab} = \left[(\Delta a^*)^2 + (\Delta b^*)^2 - (\Delta C^*_{ab})^2 \right]^{1/2}, \qquad (5.29)$$

and is illustrated in Fig. 5.23. This quantity is positive if the hue angle is greater than that of the reference and negative if the hue angle is otherwise.

The distance in this diagram is not the only factor to be taken into account, since the tolerance is not the same for all colors or in all directions, as previously stated. The dimensions of the tolerance ellipsoids should be taken into account when deciding which color distance between the reference and the sample colors is acceptable.

The Colour Measurement Committee (CMC) of the Society of Dyers and Colourists of Great Britain, in 1988, suggested the following color-difference formula, known as the CMC(l:c) equation

$$\Delta E^*_{ab} = \left[\left(\frac{\Delta L^*}{l\, S_L} \right)^2 + \left(\frac{\Delta C^*_{ab}}{c\, S_C} \right)^2 + \left(\frac{\Delta H^*_{ab}}{S_H} \right)^2 \right]^{1/2}, \qquad (5.30)$$

where ΔL^* is the lightness difference, ΔC_{ab}^* is the chroma difference, and ΔH_{ab}^* is the hue difference. The semiaxes of the tolerance ellipsoids represented by this equation have the dimensions lS_L, cS_C, and S_H, S_L is a function of the luminance L, given by

$$S_L = \frac{0.04097 \, L^*}{1 + 0.01765 \, L^*} \, , \tag{5.31}$$

if $L^* \geq 16$ or $S_L = 0.511$ if $L^* < 16$. The quantity S_C is a function of the chroma C, given by

$$S_C = \frac{0.0638 \, C_{ab}^*}{1 + 0.0131 \, C_{ab}^*} + 0.638 \, . \tag{5.32}$$

S_H is a function of the chroma C_{ab}^* and of the hue H_{ab}^*, given by

$$S_H = \frac{S_C}{TF - F + 1} \, , \tag{5.33}$$

where

$$F = \frac{(C_{ab}^*)^2}{[(C_{ab}^*)^4 + 1900]^{1/2}} \, , \tag{5.34}$$

and

$$T = 0.56 + 0.2 \cos \left| (h_{ab} + 168°) \right| \, , \tag{5.35}$$

if $164° \blacktriangleright h_{ab} > 345°$ or

$$T = 0.38 + 0.4 \cos \left| (h_{ab} + 35°) \right| \, , \tag{5.36}$$

if $h_{ab} < 164°$ or $h_{ab} > 345°$. The constants l and c are correction factors that can be chosen according to the kind of sample to be measured. The values $l = 2$ and $c = 1$ are appropriate for most visual color matches, but sometimes $l = 1$ and $c = 1$ are used.

     In this color-difference equation, the tolerance ellipsoids are assumed to be radially oriented, as shown in Fig. 5.24, which is only an approximate truth. These ellipsoids are oriented with the largest dimension along the radial (chroma) direction. They are longer and narrower in the orange region than in the green region. The size of the ellipsoids decreases with the chroma, and changes with the luminance. The actual shape of the MacAdam ellipsoids in the CIE $L^* a^* b^*$ diagram is illustrated in Fig. 5.25.

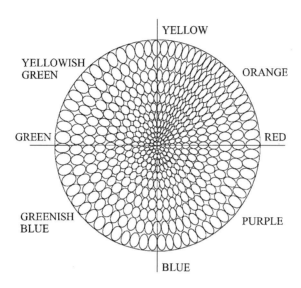

Figure 5.24 Tolerance ellipses plotted in the $a^* b^*$ plane for $L^* = 50$ in the color difference system CMC (l:c).

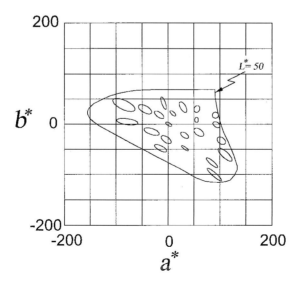

Figure 5.25 Tolerance ellipsoids in the $L^* a^* b^*$ system.

Another color difference equation was proposed by the CIE in 1994, based on the CMC(*l, c*) equation, as follows:

$$\Delta E_{94}^* = \left[\left(\frac{\Delta L^*}{k_L \; S_L} \right)^2 + \left(\frac{\Delta C_{ab}^*}{k_C \; S_C} \right)^2 + \left(\frac{\Delta H_{ab}^*}{k_H \; S_H} \right)^2 \right]^{1/2},$$

(5.37)

where ΔL^*, ΔC^*, and ΔH^* are the differences in lightness, chroma, and hue, respectively. The S_L, S_C, and S_H are the weighting functions, whose best estimated values are

$$S_L = 1,$$

$$S_C = 1 + 0.045 \; C_{ab\,ref}^*,$$

(5.38)

$$S_H = 1 + 0.015 \; C_{ab\,ref}^*,$$

where C_{abref}^* is the chroma of the reference color. The quantities k_L, k_C, and k_H are the parametric factors, for which

$$k_L = k_C = k_H = 1$$

(5.39)

for most applications, although for the textile industry the following values are preferred:

$$k_L = 2, \quad k_C = k_H = 1.$$

(5.40)

The luminance semiaxis is assumed to be constant, while the other two semiaxes are functions only of the chroma value, and the hue value is not used. The human eye can perceive CIELAB color differences of the order of $\forall$ 1.

In conclusion, the search for perfectly uniform color systems is of great practical interest and it is still a subject of research.

References

Brown W. R. J., "Color Discrimination of Twelve Observers," *J. Opt. Soc. Am.*, **47**, pp. 137–143 (1957).

Brown W. R. J. and D. L. MacAdam, "Visual Sensitivities to Combined Chromaticity and Luminance Differences," *J. Opt. Soc. Am.*, **49**, pp. 808–834 (1949).

Hunter R. S. and R. W. Harold, *The Measurement of Appearance*, 2nd. Ed., John Wiley and Sons, New York (1987).

Judd D. B., "The Unsolved Problem of Colour Perception," *Palette*, **10**, pp. 30–35 (1962). Reprinted in *Selected Papers in Colorimetry—Fundamentals,* D. L. MacAdam, Editor, SPIE Milestone Series, Volume MS77 (1993).

Judd D. B., "Perceptually Uniform Spacing of Equiluminous Colors and the Loci of Constant Hue," in *Proceeding of the Symposium on Color Metrics*, pp. 147–159 (1972). Reprinted in *Selected Papers in Colorimetry—Fundamentals,* D. L. MacAdam, Editor, SPIE Milestone Series, Volume MS77 (1993).

Kelly K. L., "Color Designations for Lights," *J. Opt. Soc. Am.*, **33**, pp. 627–632 (1943).
MacAdam D. L., "Projective Transformations of I. C. I. Color Specifications," *J. Opt. Soc. Am.*, **27**, pp. 294–299 (1937).

MacAdam D. L., "Visual Sensitivities to Color Differences in Daylight," *J. Opt. Soc. Am.*, **32**, pp. 247–274 (1942).

MacAdam D. L., "The Graphical Representation of Small Color Differences," *J. Opt. Soc. Am.*, **33**, pp. 632–636 (1943).

MacAdam D. L., "Geodesic Chromaticity Diagram Based on Variances of Color Matching by 14 Normal Observers," *Appl. Opt.*, **10**, pp. 1–7 (1971).

Muth E. J. and C. G. Persels, "Constant-Brightness Surfaces Generated by Several Color- Difference Formulas," *J. Opt. Soc. Am.*, **61**, 1152–1154 (1971).
Newhall S. M., "Final Report of the O. S. A. Subcommittee on the Spacing of the Munsell Colors," *J. Opt. Soc. Am.*, **33**, pp. 385–418 (1943).

Nickerson D., "History of the OSA Committee on Uniform Color Scales," *Optics News*, **3**, pp. 8–17 (1977).

Rheindoldt W. C. and J. P. Mennard, "Mechanized Conversion of Colorimetric Data to Munsell Renotations," *J. Opt. Soc. Am.*, **50**, pp. 802–807 (1960).

Richardson L. F., "Measurability of Sensations of Hue, Brightness, or Saturation," *Discussion on Vision*, IOP Publishing, Ltd (1960). Reprinted in *Selected Papers in Colorimetry—Fundamentals,* D. L. MacAdam, Editor, SPIE Milestone Series, Volume MS77 (1993), and in *Sources of Color Science*, pp. 241–243, MIT Press (1970).

Schrodinger E., "Grundlinien einer Theorie der Farbenmetrik im Tagessehen" *Ann. Physik*, **63**, pp. 397–515 (1920).

Silverstein L., "Investigations of the Intrinsic Properties of the Color Domain, II" *J. Opt. Soc. Am.*, **33**, pp. 1–9 (1943).

Chapter 6
Color Mixtures and Colorants

6.1 Color addition

Additive mixing of color takes place when two or more light beams with different colors are superimposed on a screen or directly on the retina of the observing eye. One example is theater stage illumination where several colored light projectors illuminate the same region. Another example is the well-known rotating top with a disc of colors. If all colors of the spectrum are in the disc, a neutral gray color is observed when the top is rotating. A third example is in color television screens, or in computer screens. Extremely small red, green and, blue dots are produced on the screen. The relative intensities of these colors produce a wide range colors for the eye.

The CIE chromaticity diagram is a useful tool to predict the color produced by different color additive mixtures. Assume that two light fields with spectral powers $P_1(\lambda)$ and $P_2(\lambda)$ are mixed. If the tristimulus values are (X_1, Y_1, Z_1) and (X_2, Y_2, Z_2), the total tristimulus values are expressed as

$$X_T = X_1 + X_2, \tag{6.1}$$

$$Y_T = Y_1 + Y_2, \tag{6.2}$$

and

$$Z_T = Z_1 + Z_2. \tag{6.3}$$

The chromaticity coordinates for the addition of the two fields are (x_T, y_T, z_T) given by

$$
x_T = \frac{X_1 + X_2}{X_1 + Y_1 + Z_1 + X_2 + Y_2 + Z_2}
$$

$$
= \frac{\sum\limits_{i=1}^{N} P_1(\lambda_i)\,\bar{x}(\lambda_i) + \sum\limits_{i=1}^{N} P_2(\lambda_i)\,\bar{x}(\lambda_i)}{\sum\limits_{i=1}^{N} P_1(\lambda_i)[\bar{x}(\lambda_i)+\bar{y}(\lambda_i)+\bar{z}(\lambda_i)] + P_2(\lambda_i)[\bar{x}(\lambda_i)+\bar{y}(\lambda_i)+\bar{z}(\lambda_i)]}, \tag{6.4}
$$

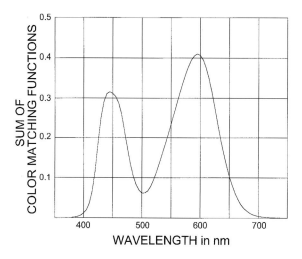

Figure 6.1 Weight w_i for a colored light beam with spectral power $P_j(\lambda)$ (sum of color matching functions).

$$y_T = \frac{Y_1 + Y_2}{X_1 + Y_1 + Z_1 + X_2 + Y_2 + Z_2}$$

(6.5)

$$= \frac{\sum_{i=1}^{N} P_1(\lambda_i)\,\bar{y}(\lambda_i) + \sum_{i=1}^{N} P_2(\lambda_i)\,\bar{y}(\lambda_i)}{\sum_{i=1}^{N} P_1(\lambda_i)[\bar{x}(\lambda_i) + \bar{y}(\lambda_i) + \bar{z}(\lambda_i)] + P_2(\lambda_i)[\bar{x}(\lambda_i) + \bar{y}(\lambda_i) + \bar{z}(\lambda_i)]},$$

and

$$z_T = \frac{Z_1 + Z_2}{X_1 + Y_1 + Z_1 + X_2 + Y_2 + Z_2}$$

(6.6)

$$= \frac{\sum_{i=1}^{N} P_1(\lambda_i)\,\bar{z}(\lambda_i) + \sum_{i=1}^{N} P_2(\lambda_i)\,\bar{z}(\lambda_i)}{\sum_{i=1}^{N} P_1(\lambda_i)[\bar{x}(\lambda_i) + \bar{y}(\lambda_i) + \bar{z}(\lambda_i)] + P_2(\lambda_i)[\bar{x}(\lambda_i) + \bar{y}(\lambda_i) + \bar{z}(\lambda_i)]}.$$

Now, when we define the weight w_i of the colored light beam i, plotted in Fig. 6.1 as

$$w_j = \sum_{i=1}^{N} [\overline{x}(\lambda_i) + \overline{y}(\lambda_i) + \overline{z}(\lambda_i)] P_j(\lambda_i)$$

$$\tag{6.7}$$

$$= X_j + Y_j + Z_j \ ,$$

we can show that

$$x_j = \frac{\sum_{i=1}^{N} P_j(\lambda_i) \overline{x}(\lambda_i)}{w_j} \ , \tag{6.8}$$

$$y_j = \frac{\sum_{i=1}^{N} P_j(\lambda_i) \overline{y}(\lambda_i)}{w_j} \ , \tag{6.9}$$

and

$$z_j = \frac{\sum_{i=1}^{N} P_j(\lambda_i) \overline{z}(\lambda_i)}{w_j} \ . \tag{6.10}$$

Thus, with these definitions, the chromaticity coordinates for the combination of two colored light beams become

$$x_T = \frac{w_1 \ x_1 + w_2 \ x_2}{w_1 + w_2} \ , \tag{6.11}$$

$$y_T = \frac{w_1 \ y_1 + w_2 \ y_2}{w_1 + w_2} \ , \tag{6.12}$$

and

$$z_T = 1 - x_T - y_T \ . \tag{6.13}$$

This result can be interpreted as a lever in equilibrium, where each of the two colors with weights w_1 and w_2 are on each end of the resultant color at the equilibrium point (Fig. 6.2). The conclusion is that any color in the line joining

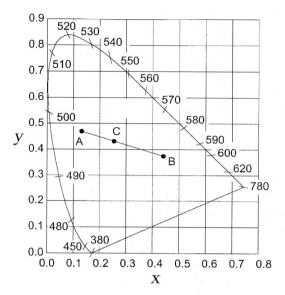

Figure 6.2 A Lever in equilibrium, with weights w_1 and w_2 on each end and resulting color at the equilibrium point.

the two added colors can be reproduced with the proper weight of these components. Generalizing this result, we conclude that with three colors—A, B, and C in the chromaticity diagram (Fig. 6.3)—any color inside the triangle can be faithfully reproduced. To find the resultant color a first step is to find the color resulting from the combination of A with B, and then combine that color with color C. Figure 6.4 shows how three colors combine by color addition. Unfortunately, these rules do not apply for the CIELAB uniform color system.

6.2 RGB color system for cathode ray tubes

A common example of color addition is in color television screens and computer monitors (Allebach, 1992; Smith, 1950) where three phosphors are used with the corresponding chromatic coordinates listed in Table 6.1. Thus, all colors inside

Table 6.1 Chromaticity coordinates x-y for some light sources.

Source	x	y
Fluorescent Lamp 4800 K	0.35	0.37
Sun 6000 K	0.32	0.33
Red Phosphor (europium yttrium vanadate)	0.68	0.32
Green Phosphor (zinc cadmium sulfide)	0.28	0.60
Blue Phosphor (zinc sulfide)	0.15	0.07

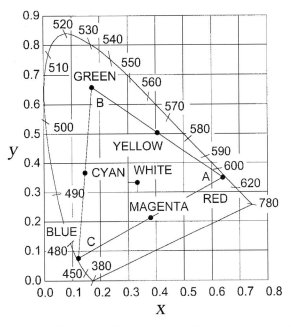

Figure 6.3 The CIE chromaticity diagram with three colors A, B, and C.

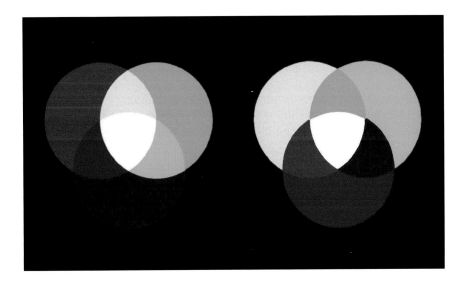

Figure 6.4 Three colors (red, green and blue) combined by color addition.

the triangle can be reproduced, but not any of the colors on the outside of the triangle. The larger the triangle, the greater the gamut of colors produced. Thus, primary colors with high purity seem desirable. Unfortunately, an increase in the purity of a light source can only be achieved by reducing the spectral width, thus decreasing the radiance.

A linear transformation can be done as described in Sec. 4.1, to transform the CIE XYZ system to an RGB system, defined by the phosphor colors. This transformation has to take into account the color coordinates for each of the three phosphor colors and also the white point coordinates for the selected observer and illuminant. To convert from the tristimulus values X, Y, Z to the R, G, B system, and vice versa for a computer display using the color coordinates in Table 6.2, we can use the linear transformation given by

$$\begin{bmatrix} R \\ G \\ B \end{bmatrix} = \begin{bmatrix} 7.0037 & -2.9266 & -1.0842 \\ -2.8445 & 5.1566 & 0.0843 \\ 0.3579 & -0.8649 & 2.8656 \end{bmatrix} \bullet \begin{bmatrix} X \\ Y \\ Z \end{bmatrix}, \tag{6.14}$$

with its inverse transformation is

$$\begin{bmatrix} X \\ Y \\ Z \end{bmatrix} = \begin{bmatrix} 0.1870 & 0.1174 & 0.0673 \\ 0.1030 & 0.2577 & 0.0314 \\ 0.0077 & 0.0631 & 0.3500 \end{bmatrix} \bullet \begin{bmatrix} R \\ G \\ B \end{bmatrix}. \tag{6.15}$$

The white point in this transformation is for the illuminant D65 and the 10-deg observer. The R, G, B values are in the range of 0 to 100. Thus, the white color generated by the set of values $R = G = B = 100$, with this matrix transformation, has to be adjusted in the display so that it is equal to the white color as observed by a 10-deg observer with a D_{65} illuminant.

Only the colors inside the triangle formed by these three points with coordinates x, y in Table 6.1 can be displayed in a color television, as shown in Fig. 6.5. The R, G, B values are negative for colors outside this triangle, but they cannot be displayed on the CRT. The brightness of each of the three phosphors is not linear with the values of R, G, and B. So, to obtain the correct brightness, a correction has to be applied by multiplying the values of R, G, and B by the proper nonlinear factor. The value of this factor depends on the kind of monitor display being used. An approximate rough correction can be obtained if we multiply the calculated values of R, G, and B by the factor F given by

$$F = 3.8 - 0.06\,Y + 0.00032Y^2 . \tag{6.16}$$

The color coordinates for some of these displays are in Table 6.2, where the coordinates for the first source (NTSC) are the same as in Table 6.1.

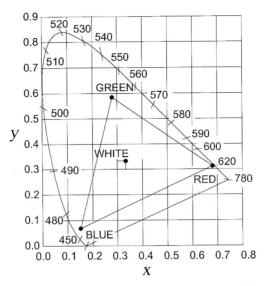

Figure 6.5 Colors that can be displayed in a color television (NTSC) are inside the triangle formed by the chromaticity coordinates of the three phosphors.

Table 6.2 Some common CRT phosphors and light sources for image displays and their *x-y* coordinates.

Source	Red		Green		Blue	
	x	y	x	y	x	y
NTSC	0.68	0.32	0.28	0.60	0.15	0.07
Computer	0.63	0.35	0.27	0.59	0.15	0.07
SMPTE	0.63	0.34	0.31	0.60	0.16	0.07
High Brightness LEDs	0.70	0.30	0.17	0.70	0.13	0.08

6.3 Color subtraction

If a colored light field is observed through a colored filter, some color components will be removed. If the spectral radiance for the light field is $P(\lambda)$ and the spectral transmittance of the filter is $\tau(\lambda)$, the effective final spectral radiance is the product of $P(\lambda)\tau(\lambda)$. It follows that if $P(\lambda)$ and $\tau(\lambda)$ do not have any wavelength range different than zero in common, the final color is black. Therefore, the process of color subtraction has to be done with continuous nonmonochromatic colors. Figure 6.6 shows the spectral characteristics of three filters—cyan, magenta, and yellow—that are used to reproduce color by the subtractive process. Ideally, each colorant transmits two-thirds of the visible

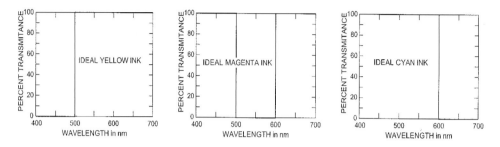

Figure 6.6 Spectral characteristics of three ideal filters that can be used to reproduce color by subtraction.

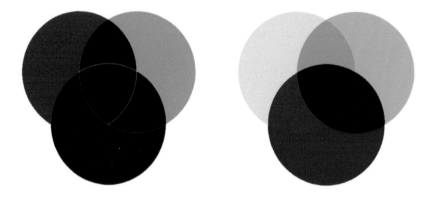

Figure 6.7 Three colored filters (cyan, magenta and yellow) combined by color subtraction.

spectrum and absorbs one-third. Figure 6.7 illustrates how these three filters combine with this process.

The subtraction process selectively removes some parts of the visible spectrum. For example, the yellow filter removes the blue color, transmitting the green and red colors. The magenta filter removes green, transmitting the red and blue colors. The cyan filter eliminates red, and transmits blue and green. Thus, by adjusting the transparency of these filters the amounts of red, green, and blue color can be controlled. Mathematically, we may express the relation between these filters using the following set of equations:

$$cyan = white - red, \tag{6.17}$$

$$magenta = white - green, \tag{6.18}$$

$$yellow = white - blue. \tag{6.19}$$

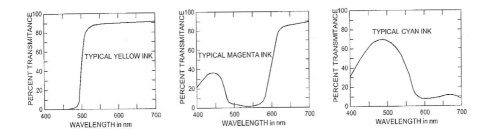

Figure 6.8 Three practical filter transmissions for color subtraction.

With these colors we have what is known as the CMY system. However, these ideal filters do not exist, so a more practical set of cyan, yellow, and magenta filters is illustrated in Fig. 6.8. Ideally, cyan, magenta, and yellow are sufficient to generate a wide range of colors by the subtractive process. For example, equal amounts of these three colors should produce black, but in practice, a dark brown color is generated. For this reason a fourth real black ink is added in many printing processes to obtain a truer color. This is called the CMYK system.

Predicting colors obtained by color subtraction is not as simple as with color addition. As shown in Fig. 6.9, cyan, yellow, and magenta are obtained inside a triangle where the three curved lines are formed. The subtractive color process is used, for example, in color photography where several layers of different colors are superimposed. It is also used by printers where three or four inks are mixed.

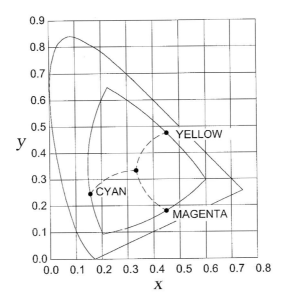

Figure 6.9 Colors obtained by subtraction using cyan, magenta and yellow.

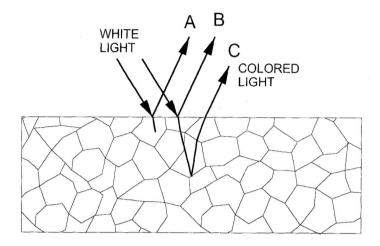

Figure 6.10 Combined addition and subtraction processes.

6.4 Complex color combinations

When two or more liquid dyes or paints are mixed, the color combination mechanisms cannot be characterized as purely additive or subtractive. In this instance, we really have a combination of the three processes as illustrated in Fig. 6.10. The colors of the two side-by-side contiguous color particles (*A* and B) combine at the eye with an addition process. If the two particles are slightly transparent, as they usually are, and one is on top of the other, the two colors of the two particles mix with a subtractive process (*B* and *C*).

6.5 Metamerism

We have seen that the perceived color of an opaque object, as defined by the tristimulus values in Eqs. (4.34), (4.35) and (4.36), depends not only on its intrinsic color given by its spectral reflectance $\rho(\lambda)$, but also on the spectral radiance, $P(\lambda)$, of the illuminating beam. A color match with any given illuminating light source is obtained when the tristimulus values X, Y, and Z are the same for the two samples being compared.

However, a perfect match under any light source does not guarantee a color match with any other light source, or by another observer. An example is shown in Fig. 6.11, where three hypothetical objects appear to have the same color under illuminant D_{65}, but not with any other illuminate. This phenomenon is called *metamerism*. When two colors with different spectral power appear to have the same color, they are said to be a *metameric* pair. A typical example of metamerism appears when a part of a car body is repainted. If the color match was made under daylight, the repair can probably be detected under street lamp

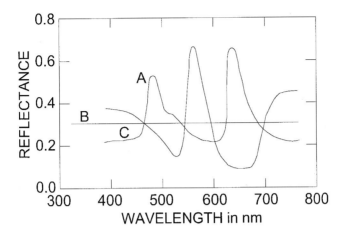

Figure 6.11 The spectral reflection of two hypothetical objects that have the same color (gray) under illumination with illuminant D_{65}. (Adapted from Judd and Wyszecki 1975).

illumination unless the same type of paint was used. Metameric pairs have the following properties:

(a) Their two spectral distributions have at least three wavelengths of the same values.
(b) Two different light source illuminations could make them appear different, but not necessarily.
(c) Two different observers could possibly see them differently but not necessarily. The CIE standard observer and two real life observers could all have different color-matching functions.

A good color match under any illumination conditions can be obtained only if the spectral reflectance curves for the two samples are identical. In principle, the presence of metamerism in two colored samples can be detected only by examination of their spectral reflectances. However, in practice, the use of three different lamps is sufficient to detect any important metamerism. The three recommended lamps used for this purpose are all daylight illuminants such as D_{65}, the color-matching lamp made by Westinghouse, and the Philips Color 84 lamp with three peaks in its spectrum.

6.6 Colorants

The word *colorant* is a general term describing any substance used to modify the color of an object by changing its spectral transmittance, or its spectral reflectance. Colorants are either *dyes* or *pigments*. Technically speaking, the difference is that dyes are soluble in the host material—typically water—while

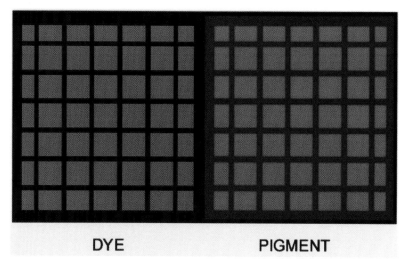

DYE   PIGMENT

Figure 6.12 Illustration of the difference between a) a dye and b) a pigment, covering an object.

pigments are not. Another difference is that dyes do not scatter light and look transparent. On the other hand, pigments do scatter light and, thus, they are opaque (see Fig. 6.12). Still another difference between dyes and pigments is that dyes are absorbed by the colored substrate and pigments need a binding agent in order to adhere to the surface. With a suitable chemical treatment, a soluble dye can be converted into an insoluble pigment. Unfortunately, the differences between a dye and a pigment are not commonly taken into consideration, frequently causing confusion. The definitions given in the dictionaries or used in some industries do not necessarily coincide with the technical terminology.

6.7 Color Matching

To make a color match with three lights is simple since only an additive process takes place. It is a little bit more difficult to make only the color subtraction process take place, but it can be done without many problems, as in color photography. However, an extremely practical problem—calculating the resultant color after mixing three paints in different proportions—is difficult. The reason for this is that both additive and subtractive processes take place in addition to many other factors that have to be considered. Most materials are colored either with dyes or with pigments. Many approaches can be used to solve this color-matching problem (Volz, 1995), for example:

(a) *Use the trial and error method.* The closest pigment to the reference sample is selected. Then, if the pigment lacks red, green, or yellow, some pigment with the missing color is added. If the mixture of pigments is too light or too dark, some black or white pigment is added. Then, the whole process is iterated several times until a satisfactory match is obtained. This is the most intuitive approach, but it also the least practical, accurate, and scientific method. It is also highly dependent on the experience of the person doing the color matching.

(b) *Use a colorimeter to measure tristimulus values.* A better approach than trial and error is to characterize the pigment mixtures of each of the basic pigments to be used by measuring the color with any color system. Then, after making a mixture, the proportion of pigments used, and the final measured color, are written down. This process is repeated for many combinations of pigments in many different proportions until a good database of all combinations is developed and is stored in a computer for future reference. This is a more rational process than the trial and error method, and produces the most reliable results. The greatest disadvantage is that the database has to be previously generated and that is valid only for those measured pigments, not for any other set.

(c) *Use the Kubelka-Munk theory.* While this is not the simplest approach, it is the most scientific. It also has many practical restrictions, as follows.

The color of a mixture of dyes or pigments is determined by the resultant reflectance $R(\lambda)$. This reflectance and the transmittance $T(\lambda)$ of a translucent sample are functions of the light-absorption coefficient $K(\lambda)$ and the light-scattering coefficient $S(\lambda)$ in the sample shown by Kubelka and Munk (1931). The absorption of light depends on the concentration of the colorant. The light scattering depends only on the microscopic structure of the colored material if dyes are used, but also depends on the colorant concentration when pigments are used. These Kubelka-Munk equations are quite complex for translucent materials, but they become much simpler when the material is opaque. In that case, the light transmission is zero and the Kubelka-Munk equation becomes

$$\frac{K(\lambda)}{S(\lambda)} = \frac{[1 - R(\lambda)]}{2\,R(\lambda)}. \qquad (6.20)$$

It has been found that this expression is quite accurate if the refractive index is close to that of air, which is true for most opaque samples. From this relation we can obtain the following expression for the reflectance $R(\lambda)$:

$$R(\lambda) = 1 + \frac{K(\lambda)}{S(\lambda)} - \left[\left(1 + \frac{K(\lambda)}{S(\lambda)} \right)^2 - 1 \right]^{1/2}. \tag{6.21}$$

In conclusion, the spectral reflectance $R(\lambda)$ is a function only of the ratio $K(\lambda)/S(\lambda)$ of the absorption and scattering coefficients. In other words, if the ratio $K(\lambda)/S(\lambda)$ of the absorption and scattering coefficients for two samples is identical for all wavelengths, their spectral reflectance $R(\lambda)$ is also identical, producing a perfect color match.

An important aspect of the Kubelka-Munk theory is that when a mixture of several dyes or pigments is used to color the material, the absorption and scattering coefficients of the mixture are calculated from the coefficients for each pigment just by their sum:

$$K(\lambda) = \sum_{i=0}^{N} c_i K_i(\lambda), \tag{6.22}$$

and

$$S(\lambda) = \sum_{i=0}^{N} c_i S_i(\lambda), \tag{6.23}$$

where c_i is the colorant concentration. For each colorant in a mixture, if the absorption coefficient $K(\lambda)$ and the scattering coefficient $S(\lambda)$ as functions of the wavelength is known, the spectral reflectance $R(\lambda)$ of the mixture can be calculated from the colorant concentrations. Conversely, if the spectral reflectance is known, the colorant concentrations can be obtained by an iterative mathematical procedure. More details on the Kubelka-Munk theory and methods can be found in the book by Judd and Wyszecki (1975).

Computer programs using different color-matching procedures have been developed to calculate the final color of a mixture of colorants, as described by Kuehni (1975), Park (1993), and McDonald (1993).

References

Allebach J. P. "Processing Digital Color Images: From Capture to Display," *Physics Today,* **45**, pp. 32–39, December, (1992).

Judd D. B. and G. Wyszecki, *Color in Business, Science and Industry,* Third Edition, John Wiley and Sons, New York, 1975.

Kubelka P. and F. Munk, "Ein Beitrag zur Optik der Farbanstriche," *Zeits. F. Tech. Physik*, **12**, pp. 593 (1931).

Kuehni R. G., *Computer Colorant Formulation*, D. C. Heath, Lexington, MA. 1975.

McDonald R. Ed., *Colour Physics for Industry*, The Society of Dyers and Colourists, Bradford, BD, 1993.

Park J., *Instrumental Color Formulation: A Practical Guide*, The Society of Dyers and Colourists, Bradford, BD, 1993.

Smith N., "Color Television,"*Scientific American*," Vol. 182, December, pp. 13 (1950).

Volz H. G. and B. Teaque (Translator), *Industrial Color Testing: Fundamentals and Techniques*, John Wiley and Sons, New York, 1995

Chapter 7
Color Measurements

7.1 Introduction

The measurement of color is a very important issue with applications in many types of industrial activities, mainly the textile, paper, leather, and graphic arts industries. The subject is so important that many articles (Kiphman, 1993), books (Berger-Schunn, 1994), and standards are devoted to this topic.

7.2 Whiteness and white standards

By definition, white is a color with high luminance and low purity. Most observers have a personal bias to classify the whiteness of several samples, but the exact order greatly depends on the illumination conditions and the environment. The ideal theoretical definition of white is that which diffuses light perfectly and has a spectral reflectance equal to one for all wavelengths in the visible spectrum (CIE, 1986). Unfortunately, this is not a practical definition, as described in the section on illuminants in Chapter 2.

Magnesium oxide, or more commonly barium sulfate, have been defined as working standard whites. These whites are prepared by pressing high-grade $BaSO_4$ powder into tablets. Recently, polytetrafluorethylene (PTFE), or pressed PTFE powder, also commercially known as Halon, Spectralon, or G-80 tetrafluorethilene resin (Weidner and Hsia, 1981), has been used. Another popular standard white is made out of ceramic tiles.

Several definitions specifying the whiteness of a material have been proposed (Judd, 1936; Ganz, 1976 and 1979; Ganz, Kurt, and Pauli, 1995). The whiteness of a material is defined by its closeness to the ideal pure white, which has a 100% reflectance and a purity of zero (MacAdam, 1934).

Obviously, the observed color depends not only on the spectral reflectance of the colored body, but also on the color of the illuminating light source. Table 7.1 shows the chromaticity coordinates and the color temperature for a white surface when illuminated by common illuminants and light sources.

The CIE formula specifying the *whiteness* W of a sample when illuminated by a D_{65} illuminant with a 10-deg field (1964) is

$$W = Y + 800(0.3138 - x) + 1700(0.3310 - y). \tag{7.1}$$

In this formula, if $x = 0.3138$ and $y = 0.3138$, the sample is neutral (gray) and its luminance is Y. The *tint* (shade) T is given by

$$T = 900(0.3138 - x) - 650(0.3310 - y). \tag{7.2}$$

Table 7.1 Color temperature and chromaticity coordinates for a white surface, using different illuminants.

Source	CIE 1931 (2°)		CIE 1964 (10°)		Color Temperature (K)
	x	y	x	y	
Illuminant A	0.4476	0.4074	0.4512	0.4059	2856
Illuminant B	0.3484	0.3516	0.3498	0.3527	4874
Illuminant C	0.3101	0.3162	0.3104	0.3191	6774
Illuminant D_{55}	0.3324	0.3475	0.3341	0.3487	5503
Illuminant D_{65}	0.3127	0.3290	0.3138	0.3310	6504
Illuminant E	0.333	0.333	0.333	0.333	5400
Direct sunlight	0.336	0.350	—	—	5335
Overcast sky	0.313	0.327	—	—	6500
North sky	0.277	0.293	—	—	10,000

If T is positive, the sample is greenish and if T is negative, the sample is reddish. These formulas have the limits of application: $Y > 70$ and $T < \pm 3$.

7.3 Optical configurations to measure reflectance

When a light beam illuminates a mirror, the light is entirely reflected at an angle following the law of reflection [Fig. 7.1(a)]. This is called specular reflection. If the illuminated surface is not completely polished but partially diffuse, as with the case of a white piece of paper, the beam is reflected in many directions, but with a strong preferential direction [Fig. 7.1(b)]. When the surface diffuses more light, like a glossy white paper [Fig. 7.1(c)], the light is reflected in all directions, but still has a preferential direction. Finally, if the surface is perfectly diffusing [Fig. 7.1(d)], the light enters the volume of the material and the reflected light does not have any preferential direction. In practice, the latter surface can be approximated by a compressed pellet of barium sulfate powder.

When measuring the color of an object, it is quite important that we measure only the diffuse reflected light and not the specularly reflected light. Only the diffusely reflected light will be colored by the object. The specularly reflected light can be avoided by using asymmetric illumination and by measuring directions as illustrated in Fig. 7.2. If the illumination is normal and the observation is at a 45-deg angle, we have the 0/45-deg configuration. On the

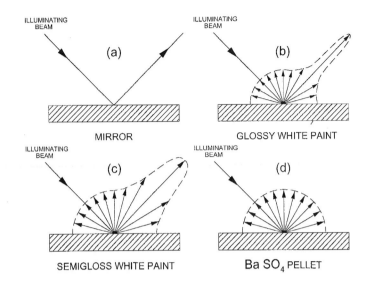

Figure 7.1 Light reflection of four types of surfaces.

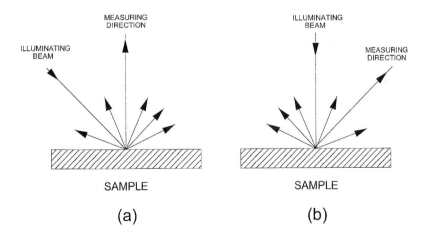

Figure 7.2 Asymmetric illumination configurations to measure color. (a) 0/45 and (b) 45/0.

other hand, if the illumination is at 45 deg and the observation is in the perpendicular direction, we have the 45-deg/0 configuration. The problem with these two arrangements is that the measurement can be affected by polarization depending on the texture of the object. A solution to this problem is to illuminate the object from several directions. For example, if the illuminating beam is in the shape of an annular cone, the measurement is made at the axis of the cone (Fig. 7.3).

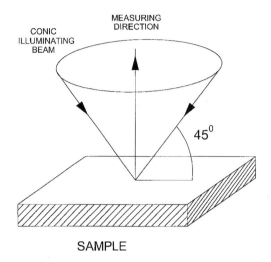

Figure 7.3 Annular illumination to measure color.

The CIE recommended two illumination configurations, using a diffusely illuminating white sphere, called an integrating sphere. In the so-called normal/diffuse (0/d) method, the illuminating beam goes directly to the measured object, and the measurement is made from the surface of the integrating sphere. A more common procedure called the diffuse/normal (d/n) method illuminates the surface of the integrating sphere, which in turn illuminates the object from all directions (Fig. 7.4). The measurement is then performed from a hole in the integrating sphere. If all specularly reflected light has to be avoided, a hole is made at the symmetrical location of the measuring hole. If this hole is covered with a small white surface, some specularly reflected light is added to the measurement. These two measurements can give an estimate of the gloss of the object, which can be defined by

$$gloss = \frac{specular\ flux}{diffuse\ flux + specular\ flux} \; , \qquad (7.3)$$

which, as a function of λ, can be shown to be

$$gloss(\lambda) = \frac{P_2(\lambda) - P_1(\lambda)}{P_2(\lambda)} , \qquad (7.4)$$

where $P_1(\lambda)$ and $P_2(\lambda)$ are the spectral-power values at the wavelength λ for the first and second measurements, respectively.

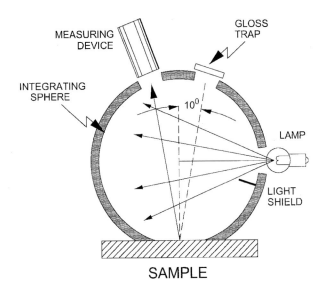

Figure 7.4 Illumination configuration d/10 using an integrating sphere to measure color.

The integrating sphere must contain light baffles to prevent light from going directly from the source, or from the integrating sphere to the detector. The integrating sphere can be made with any efficient white-diffusing material, as described in Sec. 7.2.

When measuring the reflectance color of an object, several effects could introduce errors into the results (Zwinkels, 1989, and Berns and Reniff, 1997). For example, the presence of specularly reflected light from the illuminating light source on the object to be measured can affect the result.

Another source of error could be the presence of fluorescence in the colored object. Fluorescent samples absorb short-wavelength light—mainly violet and ultraviolet—and emit it at longer wavelengths. The presence of the light emitted by the fluorescence effect changes the measured color of the object. This makes it necessary to find out whether a sample to be measured is fluorescent or not. This is done by illuminating the sample in a light booth with ultraviolet light before measuring its color.

The spectrum of the light source illuminating the colored body whose spectral reflectance is to be measured is not important since it is defined by the ratio of the reflected spectral radiance to the incident spectral radiance. It is only important that the light source emits all wavelengths of the visible spectrum except when measuring fluorescent samples. In this case, the amount of short-wavelength light producing the fluorescence is important because light sources with different short-wavelength spectrums produce different spectral reflectances.

Metallic or pearlescent objects are especially prone to introduce errors in color or when measuring reflectance. The color of these objects is highly dependent on the angles of illumination and observation. Therefore, an instrument called a spectrogoniometer is used to take measurements of several different angles. The four CIE-recommended geometries should not be used with these types of colors.

7.4 Precision and accuracy of measuring instruments

Any measuring instrument has two types of errors—random and systematic — that should be reduced to a minimum. Systematic, or bias, errors arise because of approximations and simplifications during the measuring procedure, or when some important parameters or variables are ignored. For example, warm-up time may be a source of systematic errors. Random errors occur due to the presence of unpredictable parameters that may have different values and signs every time a measurement is taken. Random errors can be reduced by averaging several measurements, but this averaging does not reduce systematic errors. An instrument with low systematic errors has high accuracy, and an instrument with low random errors has high precision. (See Fig. 7.5)

Precision has two classifications—*repeatability* and *reproducibility*. Repeatability is an evaluation of variations in the measured values with a given instrument and sampled over a specific period. The sampling can be done over a short time (a few seconds or minutes), or over along time (days or months). The samples are evaluated by taking many measurements of a stable colored body

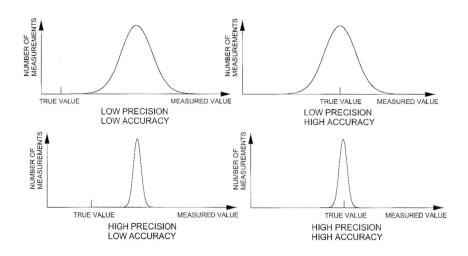

Figure 7.5 Accuracy and precision in measuring instruments.

over a short period without moving the instrument or the sample. This is important if color differences are to be evaluated for quality control. Repeatability should be of the order of 0.1 CIELAB color difference.

Reproducibility is an evaluation of variations in the measured values with changing conditions such as the operator, the laboratory, the temperature, or any other condition that might be subject to change. The values are assessed with many measurements over a long period. A good reproducibility value in a colorimeter is about 0.2, but not higher than 0.5. This is important for color matching because two objects whose color is to be matched are normally measured at different times.

Accuracy is evaluated by comparing measurements with a standard reference or with other instruments in a procedure called calibration. The accuracy procedure is not as reliable as the repeatability or the reproducibility procedures. See Table 7.1 for the classification of these errors.

Table 7.2 Classification of errors in measuring instruments, and a rough estimation of their maximum acceptable value in colorimeters.

Type of error	Related characteristics			Acceptable value in colorimeters
Systematic	Accuracy			0.5 - 1.0 %
Random	Precision	Reproducibility		0.5 - 1.0 %
		Repeatability	Short-term	0.05 - 0.1 %
			Long-term	0.5 - 1.0 %

7.5 Spectrocolorimeters

In a spectrocolorimeter, the spectral reflectance values $\rho(\lambda)$ are measured at equal wavelength separations in the visible spectral range. At each selected wavelength in the visible range, the spectral radiance values of the reflected light are divided by the spectral radiance values of the illuminating light using a perfect white diffuser. Alternatively, if a perfect standard white diffuser is not available, a white or gray sample whose spectral reflectance is known with sufficient accuracy can be used. Let us assume that the spectral reflectance for the white or gray reference sample is $\rho_{ref}(\lambda)$ and $\rho(\lambda)$ is for the colored body. Thus, if the measured reflected spectral radiance on the white reference sample is $P_{ref}(\lambda)$ and the measured spectral radiance on the colored surface is $P(\lambda)$, the spectral reflectance $\rho(\lambda)$ is given by

$$\rho(\lambda) = \left(\frac{P(\lambda)}{P_{ref}(\lambda)} \right) \rho_{ref}(\lambda). \qquad (7.5)$$

Once the reflectance $\rho(\lambda)$ has been determined, the tristimulus values and the chromaticity coordinates can be calculated using the color-matching functions. By definition, the color of an object is obtained when the object is illuminated with a light source emulating the D_{65} illuminant. Thus, the spectral reflectance is multiplied by the power spectrum of this illuminant.

The small amount of stray light going directly from the integrating sphere to the light detector should be subtracted from the measurements. To measure the spectral radiance $P_{black}(\lambda)$ of this light, a perfect blackbody is measured first. This blackbody is formed by a light trap constructed with a cavity in a hollow body with a small hole through which to observe its black painted interior. Calibrations with both a white or gray reference and a black reference should be done before using the instrument.

Thus, the real spectral reflectance $\rho(\lambda)$ of the measured sample is

$$\rho(\lambda) = \left(\frac{P(\lambda) - P_{black}(\lambda)}{P_{ref}(\lambda) - P_{black}(\lambda)} \right) \rho_{ref}(\lambda). \qquad (7.6)$$

This is the complete computational procedure to calculate the color in a spectrocolorimeter. Every spectrocolorimeter must have its own *white reference tile* from which to obtain the white reference reflectance $\rho_{ref}(\lambda)$. The absolute value for this reflectance is stored in the instrument. During the white calibration, its spectrum is adjusted so that it matches the stored spectrum within the specified tolerance. Each instrument has its own tile that cannot be interchanged with a tile from another instrument. Colored reference tiles are also convenient to check the color measured by the instrument. Green or cyan tiles are frequently used. The spectral reflectance of the reference tile must have several well-defined inflection points to be able to detect any spectral shifts in the instrument. Since the color of ceramic tiles change with temperature due to an effect known as thermochromism, the temperature must be carefully controlled within $\pm\, 2°C$.

To measure the spectral power values $P_{ref}(\lambda)$ for the white reference sample and the spectral power $P(\lambda)$ for the colored surface, the spectrum has to be formed by means of a grating or prism spectrometer. At this time, the complete spectrum values can be measured by means of a scanning slit with a photometer behind it. This instrument is called a scanning spectrophotometer. Alternatively, a CCD's one-dimensional array can be used. Some common arrangements are presented in Fig. 7.6.

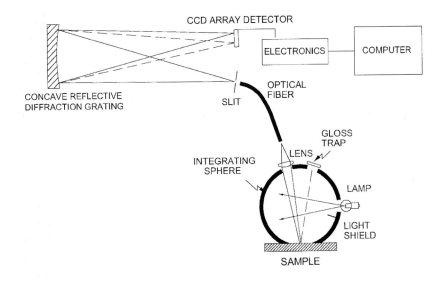

Figure 7.6 Common optical arrangements for spectrophotometers.

The measured spectral reflectance of the measured color object is used with the color-matching functions to obtain the tristimulus values *X*, *Y*, and *Z*. These values can be converted to any system such as the *L*a*b** system. The typical procedure to calculate the color in a spectrocolorimeter is illustrated in the block diagram in Fig. 7.7.

7.6 Tristimulus photocolorimeters

Tristimulus photocolorimeters take three photoelectric measurements with three different colored filters. These instruments work similarly to the visual process in the human eye, where three different color detectors (cones) are used. In general, these filters are quite complicated since all of the spectral responses—taking into account the filter's transmittance and the detector's spectral response—must be equal to the color-matching functions $\bar{x}_\lambda$, $\bar{y}_\lambda$, and $\bar{z}_\lambda$. Since each of the three photometers measures the integrated light for all wavelengths, the three measurements are proportional to the tristimulus values *X*, *Y*, and *Z*. A practical problem is that filters with spectral transmissions equal to the color-matching functions do not exist. Thus, they have to be specially designed and synthesized with the superposition of three or four filters.

We cannot "match" all colors in this way, but we can obtain enough information to identify all colors in nature. The important requirement is that the

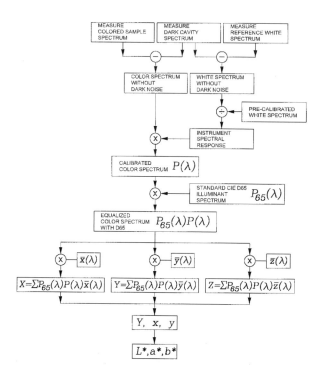

Figure 7.7 Procedure used to find the tristimulus values after measuring the spectral reflectance of a colored body.

three spectral transmittances for the three filters form a set of color-matching functions. In Chapter 8, we will see that the human eye works in an almost identical manner.

These colorimeters were very popular before the advent of modern minicomputers and microprocessors. Their accuracy was extremely poor, but the results were acceptable for color difference measurements. These colorimeters cannot detect the presence of metamerism in two samples with the same color.

Color television and CCD cameras have also been used by some authors to measure color, for example, by Corbalán et al. (2000).

7.7 Visual colorimeters

A visual colorimeter is a color-matching device with a split color field. Half of the field is covered by the body of the color to be measured, illuminated by a reference-white light source. The other half of the field is formed by a white surface, illuminated by three light sources whose colors are well determined— typically, red, green, and blue. The luminance of the three lights is varied until a good color match with the other half of the field is obtained. The three lights' brightness is manually adjusted on each lamp until a close match is obtained. The

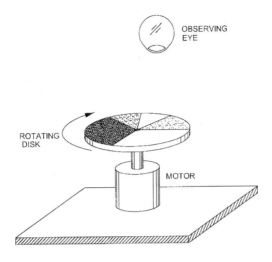

OBSERVING
EYE

ROTATING
DISK

MOTOR

Figure 7.8 Disk colorimeter.

brightness of the incandescent tungsten lamps should be adjusted by means of diaphragms, since a change in the electrical current not only changes the brightness but it also changes the color temperature.

The adjustment of this colorimeter is not simple and requires skill. This adjustment process can be simplified with other complex arrangements. For example, the white light source illuminating the colored body to be measured can be substituted by three colored lamps with the same colors as the lamps illuminating the white reference field. This arrangement adds flexibility to the system, making the adjustment simpler for unskilled operators.

Many variations of this basic arrangement have been devised to construct visual colorimeters for different applications. The disk colorimeter presents an interesting method of finding the needed proportions of a colorant for a given mixture (Fig. 7.8). This instrument takes advantage of the eye's slow response by superimposing on to it several colors painted on angular sectors of a motorized-rotating disk. It is assumed that the color of the reference sample is obtained by a color addition process. This hypothesis is more valid for pigments than for dyes. The contribution of each pigment to the resultant color is directly proportional to the magnitude of the angle in the painted sector. With this method, the hue and saturation of the sample color can be matched, but not necessarily the luminosity, unless the sample and the disk are illuminated with different light intensities.

References

Berger-Schunn A., *Practical Color Measurement*, John Wiley and Sons, New York (1994).

Berns R. S. and Reniff L., "An Abriged Technique to Diagnose Spectrophotometric Errors," in *Color Research and Application*, **22**, pp. 51–60 (1997).

CIE, *Colorimetry*, CIE Publication No. 15.2-1986, 2nd Ed., CIE Central Bureau, Vienna (1986).

Corbalán M., M. S. Millan and M. Ysuel, "Color Measurement in Standard CIELAB Coordinates Using a 3CCD Camera: Correction for the Influence of the Light Source,"*Opt. Eng.*, **39**, pp. 1470–1476 (2000).

Ganz E., H. Kurt and A Pauli, "Whiteness and Tint Formulas of the Commission Internationale de l'Eclairage: Approximations in the L*a*b* Color Space," *Appl. Opt.*, **34**, pp. 2998–2999 (1995).

Ganz E., "Whiteness: Photometric Specification and Colorimetric Evaluation," *Appl. Opt.*, **15**, pp. 2039–2058 (1976).

Ganz E., "Whiteness Formulas: A Selection," *Appl. Opt.*, **18**, pp.1073–1078 (1979).

Judd D. B., "A Method for Determining Whiteness in Paper," *Paper Trade Journal*, **103**, pp. 38–44 (1936). Reprinted in *Selected Papers in Colorimetry— Fundamentals,* D. L. MacAdam, Editor, SPIE Milestone Series, Volume MS77 (1993).

Kipphan H., "Color Measurement Methods and Systems in Printing Technology and Graphic Arts," *Proceedings of SPIE.*, **1912**, pp. 278–1998 (1993).

MacAdam D. L., "The Specification of Whiteness," *J. Opt. Soc. Am.*, **24**, pp. 188–191 (1934).

Weidner V. R. and J. J. Hsia, "Reflection Properties of Pressed Polytetrafluorethylene Powder," *J. Opt. Soc. Am.*, **71**, pp. 856–861 (1981).

Zwinkels J. C., "Errors in Colorimetry Caused by the Measuring Instrument," *Textile Chemist and Colorist*, **21**, pp. 23–29 (1989).

Chapter 8
The Human Eye

8.1 Anatomy of the eye

The human eye has been a subject of interest to many researchers for several centuries. However, the first serious studies were carried out by Helmholtz, as described in his book *Optik*. The eye studies of the nineteenth century culminated with the work by Gullstrand.

The anatomy of the human eye is diagramed in Fig. 8.1 and the main optical constants can be found in Table 8.1. The most important optical components of the eye are:

(a) *Cornea*: the transparent tissue in the front of the eye. Its ideal shape is nearly spherical, with a dioptric power of about 43. Any deviation from its ideal shape produces refractive errors. If it takes a toroidal shape, with different curvatures along two mutually perpendicular diameters, corneal astigmatism appears. The astigmatism is said to be "with the rule" if the curvature in the vertical diameter is larger than in the horizontal diameter and "against the rule" if it is otherwise. A small protuberance and thinning at the center of the cornea makes it have an almost conic shape—a defect called keratoconus. These errors are measured with an ophthalmeter or a corneal topographer.

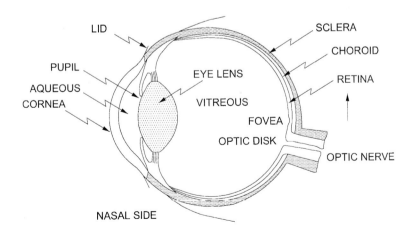

Figure 8.1 Schematics of the human eye.

(b) *Pupil*: the circular opening in front of the eye, surrounded by the iris. The pupil controls the amount of light entering the eye by increasing or decreasing its diameter. The maximum diameter of the pupil, with low illumination level is approximately 8 mm and the minimum diameter with high illumination levels is nearly 2 mm. The average diameter is between 3.5 and 4 mm.

(c) *Aqueous humor*: the liquid between the back of the cornea and the eye lens.

(d) *Eye lens* (*also called the crystalline len*s): a flexible tissue whose optical power can be modified by means of the ciliary muscles. These muscles increase the power (accommodation) of the lens to focus on close objects. When the muscles relax, the lens focuses on objects that are far away. The nucleus of this lens has a higher refractive index than its outer parts. The relaxed lens has a dioptric power of about 15 that can be increased (accommodation amplitude) by about 15 diopters in children or about 0.5 diopters in old people.

The lens contains a yellow pigment with a strong absorption in the ultraviolet region near a wavelength of 365 nm with almost perfect transparency from 550 to 650 nm, as shown in Fig. 8.2. For many reasons, the eye lens can lose its transparency producing what is known as a cataract (Lerman, 1962; Van Heyningen, 1975; Pokorny et al., 1988). To correct this condition, the eye lens must be removed. Frequently a plastic lens is inserted to replace the eye lens.

(e) *Vitreous humor*: the liquid filling most of the eye globe in the space between the eye lens and the retina. Sometimes, especially in medium or high myopic eyes, small particles float in this medium producing small images that appear to float in space, as described by White and Levatin (1962).

(f) *Retina*: the light-sensitive surface of the eye, on which images are formed. The eye's retina is formed by several layers. The most internal one, in contact with the vitreous humor, is formed by cells and fiber nerves, while the last layer, located at the back of the eye, has the light sensitive elements—the rods and cones—which will be studied in more detail in the following sections (Young, 1970).

Where the optic nerve enters the eye globe, there is a blind zone with an angular diameter of 5 to 7 deg, and at 15 deg off the optical axis on the nasal side.

Table 8.1 Average optical constants of the human eye.

Total length	24.75 mm
Pupil diameter	5.6 mm
Effective focal length	22.89 mm
Total power (unaccommodated)	58.6 diopters
Lens power (unaccommodated)	19 diopters
Corneal power	43 diopters
Corneal radius of curvature	7.98 mm
Aqueous humor refractive index	1.336
Lens refractive index at the center	1.406
Lens refractive index at the edge	1.386
Vitreous refractive index	1.337

The fovea is a small zone near the optical axis, where the retina becomes thinner and blood vessels are not present. The fovea contains only cones in a dense random array. Outside the fovea, the main light sensitive elements are the rods, which are responsible for the scotopic vision. They are much more sensitive to brightness than the cones, but they are not color sensitive and have very low spatial resolution.

Using adaptive optics techniques, astronomer David Williams and his collaborators from the University of Rochester have been able to obtain *in vivo* images of the cones, measuring about 5 μm in diameter, (Liang and Williams, 1997; Williams, 1999a and 1999b; Reiss, 1998).

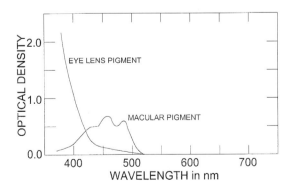

Figure 8.2 The spectral distribution of the eye lens and macular pigments.

In a small area centered on the fovea, there is a nerve layer between the vitreous humor and the cone layer, known as the *macula lutea* (yellow spot). The substance producing its yellow color is called the macular pigment and can be observed only under very special conditions. The spectral distribution of this pigment is in shown in Fig. 8.2. The macular pigment of the cones located in the central retina is less stimulated by blue light than the cones surrounding this zone, which compensate with a greater sensitivity to blue light on the macula.

The retina has a good supply of blood flowing through the retinal artery and vein both of which enter the eye at the optic disk. At this location, many small blood vessels begin to cover the retina but avoid the fovea.

8.2 Eye aberrations

As any other optical instrument with image-forming lenses, the eye has optical aberrations that limit its optical performance (Gubisch, 1967). The off-axis aberrations are not of concern for the eye, since an image is always observed on axis by quick scanning and continuous movement of the eye. However, the on-axis aberrations are important.

The axial chromatic aberration arises because the light ray focuses on different focal planes along the optical axis. Köhler (1962) devised a simple and interesting experiment to show the presence of axial chromatic aberration in the eye. To conduct the experiment, hold a card in each of your hands, and place them in front of each eye so that the straight edge covers half of each pupil. The left edge of the right-hand card must be in front of the pupil of the right eye and the right edge of the left-hand card must be in front of the pupil of the left eye. Now look at a highly colored image, for example, an image on a computer screen. You will notice that different color zones appear to have slightly different depths. This effect, called pseudostereopsis, can be also observed by some people without the cards. The effect arises because the pupils are not always centered on the optical axis (Hunt, 1991).

The axial chromatic aberration has been studied and measured by several researchers, for example, Wald and Grifflin (1947) as well as Bedford and Wyszecki (1957). The focus shift at the blue end of the spectrum due to this aberration can be as high as two diopters.

The spherical aberration of the eye appears because paraxial rays and marginal rays passing through the eye are focused at different planes along the optical axis. Many different experiments have been made to measure the spherical aberration of the eye (Koomen et al., 1949; Ivanof, 1956). As mentioned above (Liang and Williams, 1997; Williams, 1999), the spherical aberration of the eye and additional errors produced by local corneal deformations have been compensated for by means of adaptive optics.

The contrast sensitivity of the human eye has also been the subject of many investigations. For example, Williams (1985) studied the visibility and contrast of sinusoidal interference fringes near the resolution limit.

8.3 Stiles-Crawford effect

When a collimated beam of light enters the pupil, the light rays are refracted toward a common point on the retina near the optical axis. Not all rays arrive at the retina with the same incidence angle. The rays close to the optical axis are almost perpendicular to the retina, while the rays near the edge of the pupil have the largest incidence angle. The retinal angle of incidence affects the perceived luminance. The rays with the largest angle produce the smaller brightness effect on the retina. This is called the Stiles-Crawford effect.

There is a small change to the perceived color when a monochromatic light beam is incident at different angles on a given zone in the retina (Enoch and Stiles, 1961). It has been customary to call this the Stiles-Crawford effect II. It has been shown that this color change not only affects its hue but also its saturation. The changes to the perceived color are due to variations in the directional response of the three-color receptors in the retina.

8.4 Eye response to pulsating light

Alternating light fields with the same or different colors can be produced by a rotating disk with a number of apertures to permit the passing of light. The illuminated field appears to be pulsating only if the frequency is low—of the order of a few Hz—producing the phenomenon called *flicker*. When the frequency is high enough, the light pulses fuse producing the sensation of a nonpulsating light. It is interesting that the light field seems much brighter than the average brightness of the disk. This is known as the Brücke-Bartley effect. If the rotation of the disk is increased further, the flickering effect returns with a smaller magnitude, but the Brücke-Bartley effect is no longer observed. With an even greater increase in the rotation of the disk, the flickering completely disappears and the apparent luminance of the field is equal to its time-average value, also called the Talbot luminance. This is the Plateau-Talbot law. The transition of flicker to fusion occurs at the *critical fusion frequency* or *critical flickering frequency*.

In visual research, the retinal illumination cannot be directly measured. Thus, conventional retinal illumination is defined as the product of the photopic luminance in the observed object, multiplied by the area of the pupil of the eye. A *troland* is defined as the retinal illuminance produced when a surface with a luminance of one candela per meter squared is viewed through an eye having a pupil with an area of one millimeter squared, from a distance of one meter. The critical flickering frequency value depends on the retinal illumination. We see in Fig. 8.3 that the critical flickering frequency increases linearly with the logarithm of the retinal illumination. This is the Ferry-Porter law. The critical flickering frequency peaks at about 300 trolands, and decreases again once this maximum is achieved. This frequency was measured with a 2-deg white light patch surrounded by a 10-deg color field having the same average luminance.

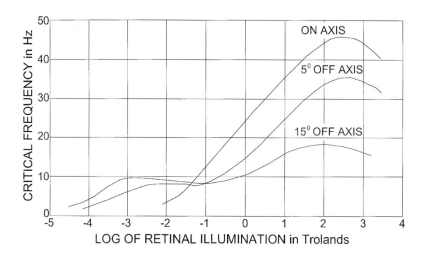

Figure 8.3 Critical-flicker frequency increases linearly with the logarithm of the retinal illumination. A white field with a diameter of 2 deg was used with a 10-deg white surround with the same luminance.

If the pulses are made up of different colors, the fusion produces a color due to the color addition of these light beams. When the pulsating frequency is low enough, the observer sees flicker. Let us consider two fields with different colors separated by a common straight boundary and pulsating with the same frequency of about 10 to 15 Hz but 180 deg out of phase—that is, one field is bright when the other is dark. The flickering is minimized when the two fields have the same luminance. This flicker method, used to measure the relative color sensitivity of the eye, was developed by Ives (1912). It is also the principle of the heterochromatic photometry methods.

Closely related to flickering, we have the so-called afterimages or aftereffects, which occur when the eye looks for a prolonged period at an image and then suddenly changes the observation target to a white surface. The previously observed image appears in negative and complementary colors (Brindley, 1963; Favreau and Corballis, 1976).

8.5 Visual detectors in the retina

There are two types of light-sensitive elements in the retina—rods and cones. The rods are responsible for night, or scotopic, vision. With higher definition than night vision, the cones are responsible for daylight color vision, or photopic vision. There are three sets of color-sensitive elements: *L-cones* for perceiving long wavelengths or red light, *M-cones* for perceiving medium wavelengths or green light, and *S-cones* for perceiving short wavelengths or blue light. The sharpest vision occurs in the central part of the retina, called the fovea, where

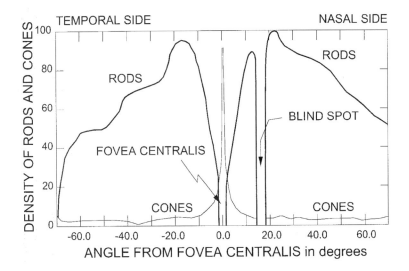

Figure 8.4 The distribution of rods and cones in the retina along a horizontal plane through the fovea.

most cones (but no rods) are located. The presence of rods begins at an angle of about 4 deg from the fovea centralis, as illustrated in Fig. 8.4. There are fewer S-cones than L- or M-cones.

The blue S-cones have the following spatial properties that make them different from the L- and M-cones (Boynton, 1996):

(a) They are sparsely distributed in the retina and are almost absent at the center of the fovea.

(b) They do not contribute to the contrast discrimination; thus they are not able to detect image borders.

(c) They do not contribute to the luminance, but, on the other hand, they do contribute very importantly to the hue and chroma—mostly yellow-blue discrimination (Eisner and MacLeod, 1980).

(d) Genes for L- and M-cones are in the X chromosome, while the genes for the S-cones are located on an autosome (chromosome 7) (Nathans et al., 1986; Nathans, 1989).

Each of the three types of cones has an associated pigment (Rushton, 1962; Rushton, 1975; MacNichol Jr., 1964; Bowmaker and Dartnall, 1980; MacLeod and Hayhoe, 1974). A good description of these pigments is found in the chapter by Rushton (1972). The absorbance spectra for these pigments was measured

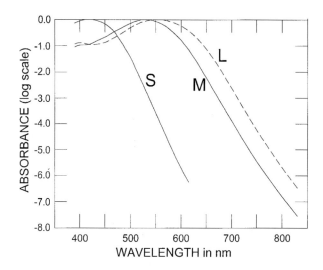

Figure 8.5 The spectral absorbance for the three cone pigments. Both scales are logarithmic.

in-situ in the outer segment using microspectrophotometry (Merbs and Nathans, 1992). In this technique, the cone receptors are placed on a microscope slide, and the light transmission of the cones is measured by passing a very small light beam through a single cone and a reference beam outside of it (Dartnall, 1983). A better method to measure cone absorbance is through a physiological method where the outer segment of a single cone is drawn inside a small suction glass electrode. Then, the electrical current response to monochromatic light of different wavelengths is measured (Schnapf, 1987). Figure 8.5 shows the spectral absorbance of the three cone pigments. The measurement of the cones pigment absorbance is important because the light detection efficiency is directly proportional to this absorbance. Table 8.2 lists the names and reflectance peaks of these pigments.

Table 8.2 Visual pigments.

Color	Pigment	Reflectance peak
Red	Eritrolabe	577 nm (yellow)
Green	Chrolabe	540 nm (green)
Blue	----	477 nm (blue-violet)

8.6 Visual chromatic defects

In 1798, John Dalton first studied color vision deficiency because he had it (Hunt et al., 1995). For this reason, color deficiency problems are sometimes known as *daltonism*. After Dalton, color-vision deficiencies were studied by many researchers (Pitt, 1944). The names for the different manifestations are formed by the greek roots—*protos*: first, *deutan*: second, *tritan*: third, for the order in which they were discovered.

Trichromats are normal color-vision persons, with three normal color receptors. *Anomalous trichromats* also have three-color receptors, but one of them is deficient. They can be *Protanomalous, deuteranomalous or tritanomalous*, if one, two, or three of the L-, M- or S-cones, respectively, are defective. Anomalous trichromats are more common than *dichromats*, which can be *protanopes, deuteranopes*, (Judd, 1945, 1949) or *tritanopes* depending on which cone is absent or completely deficient (Rushton, 1975). In protanopes, the L-cones (red) are absent (Rushton, 1963), while in deuteranopes the M-cones (green) are absent. Table 8.3 shows the relative abundance of chromatic defects.

Table 8.3 Relative abundance of visual chromatic defects.

Type of visual defect	Visual defect	Percentage of men affected	Percentage of women affected
Trichromats	None		
Anomalous Trichromats	Protanomalous	$1.08\%^2$	$0.03\%^2$
	Deuteranomalous	$4.63\%^2$	$0.36\%^2$
	Tritanomalous	$0.0\%^3$	$0.00\%^3$
Dichromats	Protanopes	$1.01\%^2$	$0.02\%^2$
	Deuteranopes	$1.27\%^2$	$0.01\%^2$
	Tritanopes	$0.005\%^3$	$0.005\%^3$
Monochromats		$0.003\%^1$	$0.002\%^1$

1. The incidence of monochromats is the lowest of all chromatic defects.
2. Percentages from Sharpe et al. (1999).
3. The incidence of tritan defects has not been clearly determined.

In protanopes, protanomalous, deuteranopes, and deuteranomalous the color deficiency is hereditary, associated to the X-chromosome, as illustrated in Table 8.4. Protan and deutan defects are the most common, also known as red-green color deficiencies.

Table 8.4 X and Y chromosomes in protan and deutan defects. X is a normal chromosome and X* is an abnormal chromosome.

Type of defect	Men	Women
Normal	X Y	X X
Affected carrier	X*Y	X*X*
Unaffected carrier		X*X

According to Wright (1952) the incidence of tritanopia (Alpern, 1976), also called the blue-green defect, is extremely low. The number is somewhere between 1 person in 13,000 to 65,000. The ratio of men to women is between 1 and 1.6. The transmission of tritan defects is not linked to the X chromosome, making it quite different from protan and deutan defects. Most frequently, this isan acquired deficiency. The congenital form seems to be less frequent than one person in a million.

One type of monochromat is the so-called S-cone monochromat, first described by Blackwell and Blackwell (1957 and 1961) and later by Alpern et al. (1971). They have rods and S-cones, but lack M- and L-cones. Reitner et al. (1991) speculated whether some kind of color vision is possible at all for these persons. This defect is linked to the X chromosome.

Completely color-blind persons are extremely rare (Lewis and Mandelbaum, 1943). Their visual functions were studied by Hetch et al. (1938), as well as Walls and Heath (1954), and Vienot et al. (1995).

In 1855, Maxwell pointed out that if two different colors appear identical to a color-deficient person, and we plot the two points corresponding to these two colors in a chromaticity diagram, the line joining the two points is the locus of colors that appear identical to the color-deficient individual. Repeating this process for many colors, we may find many straight lines in the diagram indicating the chromaticity confusion of a color-deficient person. The point ofintersection for all these lines indicates the color of the primary process not working in this person. The mathematics of this theory has been studied in detail by Judd (1945, 1949). Figure 8.6 shows the lines of constant hue for the three types of color-deficient persons, *ie.*, protanopes, deuteranopes, and tritanopes. The color-matching conditions for these persons are obviously different than for normal color-vision individuals (Walraven et al., 1966; Walraven, 1974; Breton and Cowan, 1981).

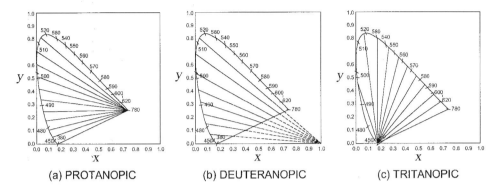

(a) PROTANOPIC   (b) DEUTERANOPIC   (c) TRITANOPIC

Figure 8.6 Lines of constant hue for protanopes, deuteranopes and tritanopes.

A metameric pair of colors, as described in Sec. 6.5, has the same color but different spectral power. Thus, if we have a metameric pair, it will also be a metameric pair for a color-deficient person.

There are many color charts designed to identify and detect color deficiencies. The most popular chart is probably the *Isihara Pseudoisochromatic Test* (Ishihara, 1954) illustrated in Fig. 8.7. People with normal color vision will see the number 74 in this pattern, while color deficient people will see the number 21.

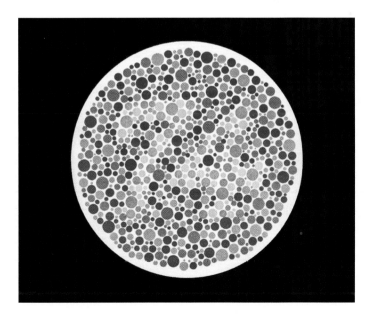

Figure 8.7 Isihara pseudoisochromatic test pattern to detect color vision deficiencies.

A good review on the subject of color deficiencies is found in the chapter by Sharpe et al. (1999).

8.7 Cone fundamentals

Basic knowledge of cone spectral sensitivities, also called *cone fundamentals*, is required for understanding color vision (Vos et al., 1990). These sensitivities were discovered after more than a century of research. In the following sections, these cone fundamentals will be represented by $\bar{l}(\lambda)$, $\bar{m}(\lambda)$, and $\bar{s}(\lambda)$.

Several methods have been used to obtain the sensitivities of human cones. One of these measuring techniques is based on the isolation of one type of cone by one of many possible procedures (Stockman, MacLeod, and Vivien, 1993). A good review of this subject can be found in a chapter by Stockman and Sharpe (1999) and in an article by Boynton (1996). Smith and Pokorny (1975) obtained estimations of the spectral sensitivities of the L-cones in deuteranopes, and of the M-cones in protanopes, using experimental conditions where the S-cones did not contribute significantly. Their measurements were later improved by Vos (1979). This approach is based on the hypothesis that in protanopia and deuteranopia one of the two longer wavelength photopigments is absent.

Another method used to measure cone sensitivity is based on the transient chromatic adaptation produced by an abrupt change of background color (Stockman, MacLeod, and Johnson, 1993; Stockman, MacLeod, and Vivien, 1993; Stockman and MacLeod, 1992). In this experiment, the 17-Hz flicker method was used to detect spectral sensitivities. An exchange of background color from blue to red was used to determine the M-cone spectral sensitivity and an exchange of background color from red to blue to determine the L-cone spectral sensitivity.

As pointed out earlier, the cone sensitivities are directly related to the absorbance of the cone pigments located in their outer segments. However, the measured cone sensitivities are different from the pigment's absorbance spectra for several reasons, mainly the presence of the macular and the crystalline pigments. The cone absorbance is directly measured, without the influence of these pigments, while the cone sensitivities are measured in the living eye, through the pigments.

There has not been a great deal of confidence in the measurements of each type of cone's absolute sensitivity. Only the relative spectral sensitivity for each one is understood. Thus, the cone sensitivities can be scaled as desired, multiplying them by any desired constant. When the cone sensitivities are plotted in a logarithmic scale, this multiplier shifts the curve up or down while preserving its shape. A common procedure is to normalize them so that the three types of cones show the same peak sensitivity. The spectral sensitivities for the three types of cones, also called fundamentals obtained by Stockman and Sharpe (2000), are based on the Stiles and Burch (1959) 10-deg color-matching functions. These are plotted in a logarithmic scale in Fig. 8.8.

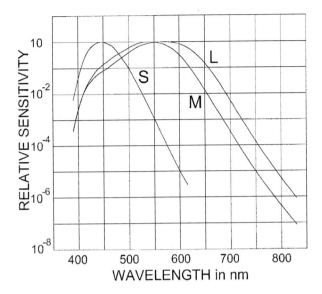

Figure 8.8 Spectral sensitivities (cone fundamentals) for the three types of cones in a logarithmic scale.

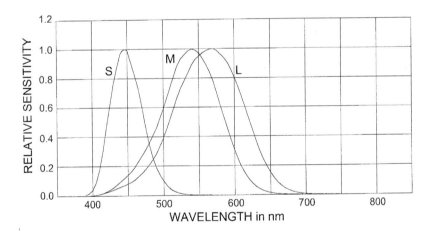

Figure 8.9 Spectral sensitivities (cone fundamentals) for the three types of cones in a linear scale.

The same sensitivities are plotted in a linear scale and are illustrated in Fig. 8.9. The logarithmic scale is preferred because the tails of the curves are very important in color perception. When the spectral sensitivities of the L- and M-cones are added, using the proper scaling multipliers, the spectral relative sensitivity $V(\lambda)$ of the eye is obtained (Fig. 8.10). These results confirm that the S-cones do not play any role in luminance detection.

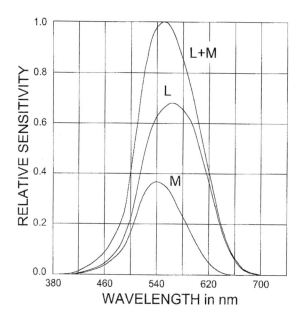

Figure 8.10 Adding the L- and M-cone sensitivities with the proper scaling constants the $V(\lambda)$ function is obtained.

8.8 Cone sensitivities related to color-matching functions

Individual cones send a signal at about the same rate that they absorb photons without regard to the wavelengths of the photons. The wavelengths only determine the rate of absorption by each type of cone, but once it is absorbed, the signal is the same. The color sensation is determined by the relative proportions in the signals provided by the three types of detectors, with the light filtered by the cone pigments. The close analogy with a tristimulus colorimeter is evident.

The magnitudes of the three cone signals can be thought of as color-matching functions for the three colors defined by the three types of cones. For example, if we knew the sensitivities of the three types of cones to each of the three primary colors r, g, and b, we could, in principle, find a linear transformation from the r, g, b space to the l, m, s space, or vice versa. So, we obtain the three color-matching functions $\bar{r}(\lambda)$, $\bar{g}(\lambda)$, $\bar{b}(\lambda)$ from the cone fundamentals $\bar{l}(\lambda)$, $\bar{m}(\lambda)$, and $\bar{s}(\lambda)$, or vice versa. These nine cone sensitivities cannot be directly measured, but if it were possible, from Sec. 4.1, we would see that the transformation matrix would be given by

$$
\begin{bmatrix} r \\ g \\ b \end{bmatrix} = \begin{bmatrix} l_r & l_g & l_b \\ m_r & m_g & m_b \\ s_r & s_g & s_b \end{bmatrix}^{-1} \bullet \begin{bmatrix} l \\ m \\ s \end{bmatrix},
\tag{8.1}
$$

where (l_r, m_r, s_r) are the coordinates of the point $(1, 0, 0)$, (l_g, m_g, s_g) are the coordinates of the point $(0, 1, 0)$, and (l_b, m_b, s_b) are the coordinates of the point $(0, 0, 1)$ as measured in the r, g, b system. In other words, l_r, l_g, and l_b are the L-cone sensitivities, m_r, m_g, and m_b are the M-cone sensitivities, and s_r, s_g, and s_b are the S-cone sensitivities to red, green, and blue light, respectively.

To find the nine elements of this matrix we can first safely define s_r as zero, since the S-cones are insensitive to red light. If we determine the values of the five unknowns (l_r/l_b, l_g/l_b, m_r/m_b, m_g/m_b, and s_g/s_b) we are left with only three unknowns, l_b, m_b, and s_b. The units for these three cone sensitivities can be arbitrarily chosen. The scaling factors only define the magnitudes for the units of each of the three tristimuli in the l, m, s space. They do not need to be directly proportional to the luminosity, radiance, or anything else. Any choice is equally valid. It is possible to make their sums for all wavelength values equal, as in Eqs. (3.7) or (4.5), so that we have a white color with equal values of the tristimuli. Another possibility is to select the values of l_b, m_b, and s_b so that the peak value for the three cone spectral sensitivities is equal to one. A change in the scaling factors would change the geometry of the linear transformation, obtaining a different set of tristimulus values, but the color matching would still be valid.

The color-matching functions are measured through the macular and eye lens pigments. So when determining the elements of this matrix, the absorption of these pigments should be taken into account. The pigment effects are different if the 2-deg or the 10-deg color-matching functions are used. For example, from 10 deg to 2 deg, it is assumed that the macular pigment's optical density changes from a peak of 0.095 to a peak of 0.35, and that the optical density of the lens's photopigment changes from 0.38 to 0.50 for L- or M-cones, or from 0.30 to 0.40 for S-cones.

Using the preceding concepts, Stockman, MacLeod, and Johnson (1993) describe a transformation to obtain the cone fundamentals from the Stiles and Burch (1959) color-matching functions, as follows:

$$\begin{bmatrix} l \\ m \\ s \end{bmatrix} = \begin{bmatrix} 0.214808 & 0.751035 & 0.045156 \\ 0.022882 & 0.940534 & 0.076827 \\ 0.000000 & 0.016500 & 0.999989 \end{bmatrix} \bullet \begin{bmatrix} r \\ g \\ b \end{bmatrix}. \qquad (8.2)$$

A correction in the blue region is made for $\lambda \leq 525$ nm, by extending the S-cone sensitivities to $\lambda > 525$ nm by the use of the function

$$\log_{10} \bar{s}(\lambda) = \frac{10{,}402.1}{\lambda} - 21.549. \qquad (8.3)$$

When adding $\bar{l}(\lambda)$ and $\bar{m}(\lambda)$ with weights equal to 0.68273 for $\bar{l}(\lambda)$ and 0.35235 for $\bar{m}(\lambda)$, the function $V(\lambda)$ is obtained as follows:

$$V(\lambda) = 0.68273\,\bar{l}(\lambda) + 0.35235\,\bar{m}(\lambda),\qquad(8.4)$$

which proves that the contribution to the luminance of the S-cones is zero.
The inverse transformation is given by

$$\begin{bmatrix} r \\ g \\ b \end{bmatrix} = \begin{bmatrix} 5.088288 & -4.064546 & 0.082501 \\ -0.123959 & 1.163679 & -0.083805 \\ 0.002045 & -0.019201 & 1.001394 \end{bmatrix} \begin{bmatrix} l \\ m \\ s \end{bmatrix}.\qquad(8.5)$$

The coordinate values r, g, b corresponding to the three points in the l, m, s space ($l = 1$, $m = 0$, $s = 0$), ($l = 0$, $m = 1$, $s = 0$), ($l = 0$, $m = 0$, $s = 1$) are listed in Table 8.5.

Table 8.5 Coordinate values r, g, b for each of the three unit points on the l, m, and s axes.

Point (l, m, s)	r	g	b
(1, 0, 0)	5.088288	−0.123959	0.002045
(0, 1, 0)	−4.064546	1.163679	−0.019201
(0, 0, 1)	0.082501	−0.083805	1.001394

In an analogous manner, the 1964 CIE color-matching functions $\bar{x}_{10}(\lambda)$, $\bar{y}_{10}(\lambda)$, and $\bar{z}_{10}(\lambda)$ for a field of 10 deg can be obtained from a linear transformation proposed by Stockmann, MacLeod, and Johnson (1993) of the $\bar{l}(\lambda)$, $\bar{m}(\lambda)$, and $\bar{s}(\lambda)$ cone spectral sensitivities by means of the transformation

$$\begin{bmatrix} l \\ m \\ s \end{bmatrix} = \begin{bmatrix} 0.236157 & 0.826427 & -0.045710 \\ -0.431117 & 1.206922 & 0.090020 \\ 0.040557 & -0.019683 & 0.486195 \end{bmatrix} \bullet \begin{bmatrix} x \\ y \\ z \end{bmatrix},\qquad(8.6)$$

with the correction in the blue region made for $\lambda \leq 520$ nm, extending the S-cone sensitivities to $\lambda > 520$ nm by the use of

$$\log_{10}\bar{s}(\lambda) = \frac{10{,}402.1}{\lambda} - 21.7185.\qquad(8.7)$$

A more recent determination of the cone fundamentals and of the transformation matrix has recently been described by Stockman, Sharpe, and Fach (1999), and by Stockman and Sharpe (2000).

A chromaticity diagram showing some stimulus excitation of equal luminance has been devised by MacLeod and Boynton (1979).

In conclusion, the processes involved in human vision are quite complicated (Neissner, 1968; Michael, 1969), but it is outside of the scope of this book to cover all of these aspects in detail.

References

Alpern M., "Tritanopia," *Am. J. of Opt. and Phys. Opt.*, **53**, pp. 340–349 (1976).

Alpern M., G. B. Lee, F. Maaseidvaag and S. S. Miller, "Colour Vision in Blue-Cone Monochromacy," *J. of Phys.*, **212**, pp. 211–233 (1971).

Bedford R. E. and G. Wyszecki, "Axial Chromatic Aberration of the Human Eye," *J. Opt. Soc. Am.*, **47**, pp. 564–565 (1957).

Blackwell H. R. and O. M. Blackwell, "Blue Cone Monochromacy: A New Color Vision Defect"(abstract only), *J. Opt. Soc. Am.*, **47**, pp. 338–338 (1957).

Blackwell H. R. and O. M. Blackwell, "Rod and Cone Receptor Mechanisms in Typical and Atypical Congenital Achromatopsia," *Vision Research*, **1**, pp. 62–107 (1961).

Brindley G. S., "Afterimages," *Scientific American*, Vol. 209, **209,** October, pp. 85–91 (1963).

Bowmaker J. K. and H. J. A. Dartnall, "Visual Pigments of Rods and Cones in the Human Retina,"*J. of Phys.*, **298,** pp. 501–512 (1980).

Boynton R. M., "History and Current Status of a Physiologically Based System of Photometry and Colorimetry," *J. Opt. Soc. Am. A.*, **8**, pp. 1609–1621 (1996).

Breton M. E. and W. B. Cowan, "Deuteranomolous Color Matching in the Deuteranopic Eye," *J. Opt. Soc. Am.*, **71,** pp. 1220–1223 (1981).

Dartnall H. J. A., J. K. Bowmaker and J. D. Mollon, "Human Visual Pigments: Microspectrophotometric Results from the Eyes of Seven Persons," *Proc. Roy. Soc. London, Ser B*, **220**, pp. 115–130 (1983).

Eisner A. and D. I. A. MacLeod, "Blue Sensitive Cones Do Not Contribute to Luminance," *J. Opt. Soc. Am.*, **70,** pp. 121–123 (1980).

Enoch J. M. and W. S. Stiles, "The Colour Change of Monochromatic Light with Retinal Angle of Incidence,"*Optica Acta*, **8**, pp. 329–358 (1961).

Favreau O. E. and M. C. Corballis, "Negative After-Effect in Visual Perception," *Scientific American*, Vol. 235, December, pp. 42–48 (1976).

Gubisch R. W., "Optical Performance of the Human Eye," *J. Opt. Soc. Am.*, **57,** pp. 407–415 (1967).

Hecht S., S. Shlaer, E. L. Smith, C. Haig and J. C. Peskin, "The Visual Functions of a Completely Color Blind Person," *Am. J. of Phys.*, **123**, pp. 94–95 (1938).

Hunt R. W. G., *Measuring Colour*, 2nd Ed., Ellis Horwood, Sussex (1991).

Hunt D. M., K. S. Dulai, J. K. Bowmaker and J. D. Mollon, "The Chemistry of John Dalton's Color Blindness," *Science*, **267**, pp. 984–8 (1995).

Ishihara S., *Tests for Colour-Blindness*, Tokyo, Kanehara Shuppan (1954).

Ivanof I., "About the Spherical Aberration of the Eye," *J. Opt. Soc. Am.*, **46**, pp. 901–903 (1956).

Ives H. E., "Studies in the Photometry of Lights of Different Colours. I. Spectral Luminosity Curves Obtained by the Equality of Brightness Photometer and Flicker Photometer Under Similar Conditions," *Phil. Mag. Ser. 6*, **24,** pp. 149–188 (1912).

Judd D. B. "Standard Response Functions for Protanopic and Deuteranopic Vision," *J. Opt. Soc. Am.*, **35**, pp. 199–221 (1945).

Judd D. B. "Standard Response Functions for Protanopic and Deuteranopic Vision," *J. Opt. Soc. Am.*, **39**, pp. 505–509 (1949).

Kohler I., "Experiments with Goggles," *Scientific American*, Vol. 206, May, pp. 63–72 (1962).

Koomen M. J., R. Tousey and R. Scolnik, "The Spherical Aberration of the Eye," *J. Opt. Soc. Am.*, **39**, pp. 370–376 (1949)

Lerman S., "Cataracts," *Scientific American*, Vol. 206, March, pp. 106–114 (1962).

Lewis S. D. and J. Mandelbaum, "Achromatopsia: Report of Three Cases," *Archive Ophthalmologica*, **30**, pp. 225–231 (1943).

Liang J. and D. R. Williams, "Aberrations and Retinal Image Quality of the Normal Human Eye," *J. Opt. Soc. Am. A.*, **14**, pp. 2873–2883 (1997).

MacLeod D. I. A. and R. M. Boynton, "Chromaticity Diagram Showing Cone Excitation by Stimuli of Equal Luminance," *J. Opt. Soc. Am.*, **69**, pp. 1183–1186 (1979).

MacLeod D. I. A. and M. Hayhoe, "Three Pigments in Normal and Anomalous Color Vision," *J. Opt. Soc. Am.*, **64**, pp. 92–96 (1974).

Mac Nichol E. F. Jr., "Three Pigment Color Vision," *Scientific American*, Vol. 211, December, pp. 48 (1964).

Merbs S. L. and J. Nathans, "Absorption Spectra of Human Cone Pigments," *Nature*, **356**, pp. 431–432 (1992).

Michael C. R., "Retinal Processing of Visual Images," *Scientific American*, Vol. 220, May, pp. 104–114 (1969).

Nathans J., T. P. Piantanida, R. L. Eddy, T. B. Shows and S. G. Hogness, "Molecular Genetics of Inherited Variation in Human Color Vision," *Science*, **232**, pp. 203–210 (1986).

Nathans J., "The Genes for Color Vision," *Scientific American*, Vol. 260, February, pp. 28–35, (1989).

Neissner U. "The Processes of Vision," *Scientific American*, Vol. 219, September, pp. 204–214 (1968). Reprinted in *Lasers and Light*, Arthur L. Schawlow, Ed., W. H. Freeman and Company, San Francisco (1969).

Pitt F. H. G., "The Nature of Normal Trichromatic and Dichromatic Vision," *Proceedings of the Royal Society of London*, **B1-32**, pp. 101–117 (1944).

Pokorny J., V. C. Smith and M. Lutze, "Aging of the Human Lens," *Applied Optics*, **26**, pp. 1437–1440 (1988).

Reiss S. M., "New Advances in Imaging for Research?" *Optics and Photonics News*, January, pp. 24–29 (1998).

Reitner A., L. T. Sharpe and E. Zrenner, "Is Colour Vision Possible with Only Rods and Blue-Sensitive Cones?" *Nature*, **352**, pp. 798–800 (1991).

Rushton W. A. H., "Visual Pigments in Man," *Scientific American*, Vol. 207, November, pp. 120–132 (1962).

Rushton W. A. H., "A Cone Pigment in the Protanope," *J. of Physiology*, **168**, pp. 345–359 (1963).

Rushton W. A. H., "Visual Pigments in Man," in *Handbook of Sensory Physiology*, H. J. A. Dartnall, Ed., Springer-Verlag, New York (1972).

Rushton W. A. H., "Visual Pigment and Color Blindness," *Scientific American*, Vol. 232, March, pp. 64–77 (1975).

Schnapf J. L., T. W. Kraft and D. A. Baylor, "Spectral Sensitivity of Human Cone Photoreceptors," *Nature*, **323**, pp. 439–441 (1987).

Sharpe L. T., A. Stockman, H. Jägle and J. Nathans, "Opsin Genes, Cone Photopigments, Color Vision, and Color Blindness," in *Color Vision. From Genes to Perception*, K. R. Gegenfurtner and L. T. Sharpe, Eds., Cambridge University Press, Cambridge (1999).

Smith V. and J. Pokorny, "Spectral Sensitivity of the Foveal Cone Photopigments Between 400 and 500 nm," *Vision Res.*, **15**, pp. 161–171 (1975).

Stiles, W. S., and J. M. Burch, "NPL Colour-Matching Investigation: Final Report (1958)," *Optica Acta*, **6**, pp. 1–26 (1959).

Stockman A. and D. I. A. MacLeod, "A Change in Color Produced by an Invisibly Flickering Light: a Compressive Non-Linearity in the S-Cone Pathway," *Investigative Ophthalmology and Visual Science (Supplement)*, **33**, p. 756 (1992).

Stockman A., D. I. A. MacLeod and N. E. Johnson, "Spectral Sensitivities of the Human Cones," *J. Opt. Soc. Am. A*, **10**, 2491–2521 (1993).

Stockman A., D. I. A. MacLeod and J. A. Vivien, "Isolation of the Middle- and Long-Wavelength Sensitive Cones in Normal Trichromats," *J. Opt. Soc. Am. A*, **10**, 2471–2490 (1993).

Stockman A. and L. T. Sharpe, "Cone Spectral Sensitivities and Color Matching," in *Color Vision. From Genes to Perception*, K. R. Gegenfurtner and L. T. Sharpe, Eds., Cambridge University Press, Cambridge (1999).

Stockman A., and L. T. Sharpe, "Tritanopic Color Matches and the Middle- and Long-Wavelength-Sensitive Cone Spectral Sensitivities," *Vision Research*, **40**, 1739–1750 (2000).

Stockman, A., L. T. Sharpe and C. C. Fach, "The Spectral Sensitivity of the Human Short-Wavelength Cones," *Vision Research*, **39**, pp. 2901–2927 (1999).

Stockman, A., and L. T. Sharpe, "Spectral Sensitivities of the Middle- and Long-Wavelength Sensitive Cones Derived from Measurements in Observers of Known Genotype," *Vision Research*, **40**, pp. 1711–1737 (2000).

Van Heyningen R., "What Happens to the Human Lens in Cataract," *Scientific American*, Vol. 233, December, pp. 70–81 (1975).

Vienot F., H. Brettel, L. Ott, M. B. A. Ben and J. D. Mollon, "What do Colour-Blind People See? [letter]," *Nature*, **376**, pp. 127–128 (1995).

Vos J. J., "Colorimetric and Photometric Properties of a 2-deg Fundamental Observer," *Color Res. Appl.*, **3**, pp. 125–128 (1979).

Vos J. J., O. Estévez and P. L. Walraven, "Improved Color Fundamentals Offer a New View on Photometric Additivity," *Vision Research*, **30**, 936–943 (1990).

Wald G. and D. R. Griflin, "The Change in Refractive Power of the Human Eye in Dim and Bright Light," *J. Opt. Soc. Am.* **37**, 321–336 (1947).

Walls G. L. and G. G. Heath, "Typical Total Color Blindness Reinterpreted," *Acta Ophthalmologica*, **32**, pp. 253–297 (1954).

Walraven P. L., "A Closer Look at the Tritanopic Confusion Point," *Vision Research*, **14**, pp. 1339–1343 (1974).

Walraven P. L., A. M. J. Van Hout and H. J. Leebeek, "Fundamental Response Curves of a Normal and a Deuteranomolous Observer Derived from Chromatic Adaptation," *J. Opt. Soc. Am.*, **56**, 125–127 (1966).

White H. E. and P. Levatin, "Floaters in the Eye," *Scientific American*, Vol. 206, June, pp. 119–127 (1962).

Williams D. R., "Visibility of Interference Fringes Near the Resolution Limit," *J. Opt. Soc. Am. A*, **2**, 1087–1093 (1985).

Williams D. R., "The Trichromatic Cone Mosaic in the Human Eye," in *Color Vision. From Genes to Perception*, K. R. Gegenfurtner and L. T. Sharpe, Eds., Cambridge University Press, Cambridge (1999a).

Williams D. R., "Wavefront Sensing and Compensation for the Human Eye," in *Adaptive Optics Engineering Handbook*, R. K. Tyson, Ed., Marcel Dekker, Inc., New York (1999b).

Wright W. D., "The Characteristics of Tritanopia," *J. Opt. Soc. Am.*, **42**, 509–521 (1952).

Young R. W., "Visual Cells," *Scientific American*, Vol. 223, October, pp. 80–91 (1970).

General References

Books

American Society for Testing and Materials, *ASTM Standards on Color and Appearance Measurement*, 3rd Ed., Amer. Soc. for Testing and Materials, New York, 1991.

Abney W. D. W., *Researches in Colour Vision,* Longmans, London, 1913.

Berger-Schunn A., *Practical Color Measurement*, John Wiley and Sons, New York, 1994.

Berns R. S., F. W. Billmeyer and M. Saltzman, *Billmeyer and Saltzman's Principles of Color Technology*, John Wiley and Sons, New York, 2000.

Billmeyer F. W., Jr., and M. Saltzman, *Principles of Color Technology*, 2nd. Ed., John Wiley and Sons, New York, 1981.

Boynton R. M., *Human Color Vision*, Holt, Rinehart and Winston, New York, 1979.

Byrne A., R. H. David and A. Byrne, Eds., *Readings on Color: The Science of Color*, MIT Press, Massachusetts, 1997.

CIE, *Colorimetry (Publication 15.2)*, Commission International de l'Eclairage (CIE), Central Bureau of the CIE, Vienna, 1986.

DeCusatis C., *Handbook of Applied Photometry*, American Institute of Physics, Springer, New York, Berlin, 1999.

Doherty P. and D. Rathjen, *The Magic Wand and Other Bright Experiments on Light and Color*, John Wiley and Sons, New York, 1995.

Fairchild M. D., *Color Appearance Models*, Addison Wesley, New York, 1997.

Fortner B., T. E. Meyer and T. Meyer, *Number by Colors: A Guide to Using Color to Understand Technical Data*, Springer Verlag, Berlin, 1997.

Gegenfurtner K. R. and L. T. Sharpe, Eds., *Color Vision. From Genes to Perception,* Cambridge University Press, Cambridge, 1999.

Giorgianni E. J. and T. E. Madden, *Digital Color Management: Encoding Solutions*, Addison Wesley, New York, 1998.

Hunt R. W. G., *Measuring Colour*, 2nd Ed., Ellis Horwood, Sussex, 1991.

Hunt R. W. G., *The Reproduction of Colour*, Fountain Press Ltd., London, 1996.

Hunter R. S. and R. W. Harold, *The Measurement of Appearance*, 2nd. Ed., Ellis John Wiley and Sons, New York, 1987.

Judd D. B. and G. Wyszecki, *Color in Business, Science and Industry,* Third Edition, John Wiley and Sons, New York, 1975.

Kaiser P. K. and R. M. Boynton, *Human Color Vision, Second Edition..* Optical Society of America, Washington, DC, 1996.

LeGrand Y., *Light, Colour and Vision,* 2nd ed., Chapman and Hall, London, 1968.

MacAdam D. L., *Color Measurement: Theme and Variations,* 2nd Ed., Springer Verlag, Berlin, 1985.

MacAdam D. L., Ed., *Selected Papers in Colorimetry—Fundamentals,* SPIE Milestone Series, Volume MS 77, 1993.

Minnaert M. G. J., *The Nature of Light and Color in the Open Air,* Dover Publications, Inc., New York, 1954.

Minnaert M. G. J. and L. Seymour, *Light and Color in the Outdoors,* Springer Verlag, Berlin, 1993.

Mueller C. G., M. Rudolph, *Light and Vision,* Time-Life International, 1963.

Nassau K., Ed., *The Physics and Chemistry of Color: The Fifteen Causes of Color,* John Wiley and Sons, New York, 1983.

Nassau K., Ed., *Color for Science, Art and Technology,* Elsevier Science, B. V., 1998.

Parsons J. H. *An Introduction to Colour Vision,* 2nd ed., Cambridge University Press, Cambridge, 1924.

Rood O. N., *Modern Chromatics, with Applications to Art and Industry,* D. Appleton and Co, New York, 1879.

Sanguine S. J. and R. E. N. Horne, Eds., *The Colour Image Processing Handbook*, Chapman and Hall, London, 1998.

Stiles W. S., *Mechanisms of Colour Vision,* Academic, London, 1978.

Tilley R. J. D., *Color and the Optical Properties of Materials: An Exploration of the Relationships Between Light, the Optical Properies of Materials and Color,* John Wiley and Sons, New York, 2000.

Volz H. G. and B. Teaque (Translator), *Industrial Color Testing: Fundamentals and Techniques*, John Wiley and Sons, New York, 1995

Williamson S. J. and Z. C. Herman, *Light and Color in Nature and Art,* John Wiley and Sons, New York, 1983.

Wyszecki G. and W. S. Stiles, *Color Science: Concepts and Methods, Quantitative Data and Formulae,* 2nd Ed., Wiley, New York, 1982.

Articles from Scientific American

Beck J., "The Perception of Surface Color," *Scientific American,* Vol. 233, August, pp. 62–75 (1975).

Brindley G. S., "Afterimages," *Scientific American,* Vol. 209, October, pp. 85–91 (1963).

Brou, P., T., R. S., L. Linette and Y. L. Jerome, "The Colors of Things," *Scientific American,* Vol. 255, September, pp. 80–87 (1986).

Clevenger S., "Flower Pigments," *Scientific American,* Vol. 209, October, pp. 84–92 (1963).

Evans R. M., "Maxwell's Color Photograph," *Scientific American,* Vol. 205, November, pp. 112–128 (1961).

Favreau O. E. and M. C. Corballis, "Negative Aftereffects in Visual Perception," *Scientific American,* Vol. 235, December, pp. 42–48 (1976).

Gregory R. L., "Visual Illusions," *Scientific American,* Vol. 219, November, pp. 66–76 (1968).

Horridge A., "The Compound Eye of Insects," *Scientific American,* Vol. 237, July, pp. 108–120 (1977).

Kohler I., "Experiments with Goggles," *Scientific American,* Vol. 206, May, pp. 63–72 (1962).

Land E. H., "Experiments in Color Vision," *Scientific American,* Vol. 200, May pp. 84–99 (1959).

Land E. H., "The Retinex Theory of Color Vision," *Scientific American,* Vol. 237, December, pp. 108–128 (1977).

Lerman S., "Cataracts," *Scientific American*, Vol. 206, March, pp. 106–114 (1962).

Levine J. S. and Mac Nichol Jr. E. F., "Color Vision in Fishes," *Scientific American*, Vol. 246, February pp. 108–117 (1982).

MacNichol E. F. Jr., "Three Pigment Color Vision," *Scientific American*, Vol. 211, December, pp. 48–56 (1964).

Michael C. R., "Retinal Processing of Visual Images," *Scientific American*, Vol. 220, May, pp. 104–114 (1969).

Milne L. J. and M. J. Milne, "How Animals Change Color," *Scientific American*, Vol. 186, March, pp. 64–67 (1952).

Nathans J., "The Genes for Color Vision," *Scientific American*, Vol. 260, February, pp. 28–35, (1989)

Nassau K., "The Causes of Color," *Scientific American*, Vol. 243, October, pp. 124–152 (1980).

Neisser U. "The Processes of Vision," *Scientific American*, Vol. 219, September pp. 204–214 (1968). Reprinted in *Lasers and Light,* Arthur L. Schawlow, Ed., W. H. Freeman and Company, San Francisco (1969).

Newman E. A. and P. H. Hartline, "The Infrared Vision of Snakes," *Scientific American*, Vol. 246, March, pp. 98–107 (1982).

Nijhout H. F., "The Color Patterns of Butterflies and Moths," *Scientific American*, Vol. 245, November, pp. 104–115 (1981).

Pettigrew J. D., "The Neurophysiology of Binocular Vision." *Scientific American*, Vol. 227, August, pp. 84–95 (1972).

Rushton W. A. H., "Visual Pigments in Man," *Scientific American*, Vol. 207, November, pp. 120–132 (1962).

Rushton W. A. H., "Visual Pigment and Color Blindness," *Scientific American*, Vol. 232, March, pp. 64–77 (1975).

Smith N., "Color Television," *Scientific American*," Vol. 182, December, pp. 13–15 (1950).

Thimann K. V., "Autumn Colors," *Scientific American*, Vol. 182, October, pp. 40 (1950).

Timberge N., "Defense by Color," *Scientific American*, Vol. 197, October, pp. 48–54 (1957).

Van Heyningen R., "What Happens to the Human Lens in Cataract," *Scientific American,"* Vol. 233, December, pp. 70–81 (1975).

Wallach H., "The Perception of Neutral Colors," *Scientific American*, Vol. 208, pp. 107–116, January (1963).

White H. E. and P. Levatin, "Floaters' in the Eye," *Scientific American*, Vol. 206, June, pp. 119–127 (1962).

Wolfe J. M., "Hidden Visual Processes," *Scientific American,"* Vol. 248, February, pp. 72–85 (1983).

Young R. W., "Visual Cells," *Scientific American,"* Vol. 223, October, pp. 80–91 (1970).

Review Articles

Boynton R. M., "Color Vision," *Annual Review of Psychology,* **39,** pp. 69–100, 1988.

Boynton R. M., "History and Current Status of a Physiologically Based System pf Photometry and Colorimetry," *J. Opt. Soc. Am. A,* **13,** pp.1609–1621 (1996).

Luria S. M., "Color Vision," *Physics Today,* Vol. 19, March (1966).

MacAdam D. L., "Color Photography," *Physics Today,* Vol. 20, January (1967).

MacAdam D. L., "Color Essays," *J. Opt. Soc. Am.,* **65**, pp. 483–493 (1975).

Mollon J. D. "Color Vision," *Annual Review of Psychology,* **33**, pp. 41–85 (1982).

Robertson A. R. "Color Perception," *Physics Today,* Vol. 45, December, pp. 24–29 (1992).

Wald, G., "Human Vision and the Spectrum," *Science*, **101**, pp. 653–658 (1945).

Wintringham W. T., "Color Television and Colorimetry," *Proceedings of the IRE*, **39**, pp. 1135–1172 (1951).

Internet sites

International Commission on Illumination
   This is the official site if the International Commission on Illumination (CIE). It contains the information on all color standards.

http://www.hike.te.chiba-u.ac.jp/ikeda/CIE/home.html

Efg's Color Library
> This page contains a very large amount of color information, with many web addresses, classified in three subjects: (a) General Color Information, (b) Color Science/Theory and (c) Color and Computers.

http://www.efg2.com/Lab/Library/Color/default.htm

Color and Vision Research Laboratories, San Diego:
> These Web pages provide a very good library of easily downloadable standard data sets relevant to color and vision research. The focus of this site is primarily scientific and technical.

http://www.cvrl.org

The Coloring Info Pages:
> This site contains some interesting information. Of special interest are some calculators to convert coordinates between different color systems.

http://www.colorpro.com/info/

Color Science:
> This web page by the Department of Physics and Astronomy of the Stephen F. Austin State University has a lot of interesting educational information about color science.

http://www.physics.sfasu.edu/astro/color.html

Coordinate Converter:
> This is a web page by the Lappeerants University of Technology in Finland. It has several interesting demonstrations and color coordinate converters. It includes some links to other color sites.

http://www.it.lut.fi/research/color/coordinates/coordinates.html

Linocolor:
> This page is by the Linocolor Company. It has some interesting educative color pages.

http://www.linocolor.com/

Radiation and Spectra: Study Guide
> This page provides some information about light phenomena, optical radiation and spectra.

http://aurora.phys.utk.edu/~daunt/study_guides/Rad&Spectra.html

Standard Illuminants:

This is a page by the Department of Agricultural Engineering of the University of Illinois. It contains data about the official standard illuminants.

http://www.age.uiuc.edu/age315/illumination/ill10.htm

Index

Daniel Malacara obtained his B.Sc. in Physics in 1961 from the National University of Mexico and his Ph.D. in Optics in 1965 from the University of Rochester. At that time, he joined the Institute of Astronomy of the National University of México, and in 1972 he joined the *Instituto Nacional de Astrofísica, Optica y Electrónica*. He promoted the creation of the *Centro de Investigaciones en Optica* and served as its first General Director from 1980 to 1989. He was the Rudolf and Hilda Kingslake Professor at the University of Rochester in 1989 and 1990.

Dr. Malacara's central field of activity is optical testing and optical instrumentation. His scientific contributions include more than one hundred papers in well-known optics journals, and he has been the author and editor of several books in optics. His most widely acknowledged book, *Optical Shop Testing,* has been translated into several languages.

He is a fellow of both the International Society for Optical Engineering (SPIE), and the Optical Society of America (OSA). He has been vice president of the International Commission for Optics (ICO), a topical Editor for *Applied Optics*, and he has been a co-organizer of many international scientific meetings. In 1986 he received the Mexican National Prize for Technology; in 1994, SPIE's Conrady Award; and, in 1997, the ICO Galileo Galilei Prize.